GCSE English

Blood Brothers

by Willy Russell

Class conflict, sibling rivalry, love, betrayal and singing milkmen...
writing about *Blood Brothers* is a serious business.

Luckily, this brilliant CGP Workbook is here to help. Inside, you'll find all the
practice questions you could ever dream of — they'll test you on the plot,
characters, themes, context, dramatic techniques and more!

There's also plenty of exam practice and tips to help you improve your essays.
When a book's this good, you'll never want to be separated from it.

The Workbook

CONTENTS

How to Use this Book 1

Section One — Analysis of Acts

Act One... 2
Act Two 7
Skills Focus: Using Quotes 12
Skills Focus: P.E.E.D. 13

Section Two — Characters

Mrs Johnstone.. 14
Mr and Mrs Lyons 15
Mickey Johnstone 16
Edward Lyons 17
Linda... 18
Sammy Johnstone 19
The Narrator 20
Skills Focus: Making Links 21
Practice Questions 22

Section Three — Context and Themes

Liverpool in the Late Twentieth Century 23
Money and Social Class... 24
Fate and Superstition 26
Childhood and Growing Up 28
Friendship 29
Identity.. 30
Gender 31
Skills Focus: Writing about Context 32
Practice Questions.. 33

CONTENTS

Section Four — The Writer's Techniques

Structure in 'Blood Brothers' 34
Form in 'Blood Brothers' 35
Language in 'Blood Brothers' 36
Atmosphere and Mood 37
Imagery and Symbolism 38
'Blood Brothers' on the Stage 39
Skills Focus: Staging and Dramatic Techniques 40
Practice Questions 41

Section Five — Exam Buster

Understanding the Question 42
Making a Rough Plan 43
Making Links 44
Structuring Your Answer 45
Introductions and Conclusions 46
Writing about Context 47
Linking Ideas and Paragraphs 48
Marking Answer Extracts 49
Marking a Whole Answer 51
Skills Focus: Writing Well 53
Practice Questions 54

Answers 55
The Characters from 'Blood Brothers'
'Blood Brothers' Cartoon

Published by CGP

Editors:
Emma Cleasby
Rose Jones
Louise McEvoy

With thanks to Izzy Bowen and Nicola Woodfin for the proofreading.
With thanks to Jan Greenway for the copyright research.

Acknowledgements:

With thanks to Arenapal for permission to use the images on pages 1, 8, 14, 16 and 19.

With thanks to Photostage for permission to use the images on the cover and on pages 7 and 35.

With thanks to Rex Features for permission to use the images on pages 3, 10, 26, 31 and 36.

With thanks to Enda Markey and Kurt Sneddon for permission to use the images on pages 5, 15, 17, 18, 20, 24, 28 and 38.

*Every effort has been made to locate copyright holders and obtain permission to reproduce sources.
For those sources where it has been difficult to trace the copyright holder of the work, we would be grateful
for information. If any copyright holder would like us to make an amendment to the acknowledgements,
please notify us and we will gladly update the book at the next reprint. Thank you.*

ISBN: 978 1 78294 781 3

Printed by Elanders Ltd, Newcastle upon Tyne.

Clipart from Corel®

Based on the classic CGP style created by Richard Parsons.

Text, design, layout and original illustrations © Coordination Group Publications Ltd. (CGP) 2017

How to Use this Book

Practise the four main skills you'll need for the exam

Each question tests <u>one or more</u> of the <u>four skills</u> you'll be tested on in the <u>exam</u>. You'll need to:

1) Write about the text in a <u>thoughtful way</u>, <u>picking out</u> appropriate <u>examples</u> and <u>quotations</u> to back up your opinions.

2) <u>Identify</u> and <u>explain</u> features of the play's <u>form</u>, <u>structure</u> and <u>language</u>. Using <u>subject terminology</u>, show how the author uses these to create <u>characters</u> and <u>settings</u>, explore <u>themes</u> and affect the <u>audience's reactions</u>.

3) Write about the play's <u>context</u> in your exam.

4) Write in a <u>clear</u>, <u>well-structured</u> and <u>accurate</u> way. <u>5%</u> of the marks in your English Literature GCSE are for <u>spelling</u>, <u>punctuation</u> and <u>grammar</u>.

Most exam boards will want you write about context. Ask your teacher if you're not sure.

Use this workbook with or without the CGP Text Guide

1) This workbook is perfect to use with CGP's <u>Text Guide</u> for *Blood Brothers*. The workbook matches <u>each section</u> of the Text Guide, so you can test your knowledge <u>bit by bit</u>.

2) You can also use this book <u>by itself</u>. It covers all the <u>important</u> parts of the text — <u>plot</u>, <u>characters</u>, <u>context</u>, <u>themes</u> and <u>writer's techniques</u>.

3) The questions refer to the text <u>in detail</u> — you'll need a <u>copy</u> of the play to make the most of the workbook.

© Eric Richmond/ArenaPAL

It prepares you for the exam every step of the way

1) The exam section is jam-packed with <u>useful advice</u>. It <u>guides</u> you through how to tackle the exam, from understanding the questions to building great answers. There's also an easy-to-read <u>mark scheme</u>, which you can use to mark <u>sample answers</u> and improve answers of your <u>own</u>.

2) There are four pages of <u>practice exam questions</u> spread across the book. They give you the opportunity to use what you've revised in each section to write a <u>realistic answer</u>.

3) <u>Exam tips</u> and extra <u>practice exam questions</u> are included throughout the book. There are also helpful <u>revision tasks</u> designed to get you thinking more creatively. These are marked with <u>stamps</u>.

4) You can find <u>answers</u> to all of the <u>questions</u> and <u>tasks</u> at the back of the book.

5) Each section contains at least one '<u>Skills Focus</u>' page. These pages help you to practise important skills <u>individually</u>. You can tackle them in <u>any order</u> and prioritise the skills you find the <u>hardest</u>.

It's time to Russell up some answers...

Now you're up to speed on how to use this book, you're ready to grab a copy of the play and get going on some workbook questions. You can do the sections in any order — pick one that you like the look of and get stuck in.

Section One — Analysis of Acts

Act One

Mrs Johnstone and Mrs Lyons make an agreement

Q1 How does Russell create tension at the start of Act One?
Support your answer with an example.

....

....

....

Q2 Read from when Mrs Johnstone sings "**Once I had a husband**" until
she says "**Milk Shake for the Baby**", then answer the questions below.

a) How has Mr Johnstone's absence affected Mrs Johnstone's life?

....

b) What is the effect of the Milkman interrupting Mrs Johnstone's song?

....

Q3 Put these events in order by numbering the boxes. The first one has been done for you.

Mrs Johnstone promises to give Mrs Lyons one of the twins. ☐

Mrs Johnstone discovers that she is having twins. 1

Mrs Lyons promises to let Mrs Johnstone see her baby every day. ☐

Mrs Lyons comes up with a plan to deceive her husband about the baby. ☐

Mrs Lyons decides to take one of the twins from Mrs Johnstone. ☐

Q4 Mrs Lyons manipulates Mrs Johnstone into giving up one of
the twins. In your own words, explain how she does this.

....

....

....

Q5 How does Mrs Lyons react when Mrs Johnstone agrees to give one of the twins to her?

....

....

Mrs Lyons breaks the agreement

Q1 Why do you think Russell chose to have the Catalogue Man and the other creditors arrive immediately after Mrs Johnstone brings home the twins?

....

....

Q2 Read from when Mrs Johnstone says "**Ah... he's lovely**" until Mrs Lyons says "**you will kill them**". Decide whether each statement is **true** or **false**, and find a short quote to support your answer.

a) Mr Lyons doesn't care about Mrs Johnstone's feelings. **True:** ☐ **False:** ☐

Quote: ....

b) Mr Lyons leaves decisions about household matters to his wife. **True:** ☐ **False:** ☐

Quote: ....

c) Mrs Lyons feels threatened by Mrs Johnstone. **True:** ☐ **False:** ☐

Quote: ....

Q3 Read the paragraph below and fill in the gaps using words from the box.

Mrs Johnstone is confused when .... dismisses her. She begins

to .... when she realises that she won't be able to support her

family without a .... Mrs Lyons tries to pay her to leave, forcing

the .... given to her by .... into Mrs Johnstone's

hands. When Mrs Johnstone tries to take the ...., Mrs Lyons pulls

her away from the cot, claiming that .... belongs to her.

| Mrs Lyons |
| money |
| Edward |
| job |
| Mickey |
| son |
| baby |
| panic |
| children |
| Mr Lyons |

Q4 Why doesn't Mrs Johnstone go to the police when Mrs Lyons breaks their agreement?

© Nils Jorgensen/REX/Shutterstock

....

....

....

....

Section One — Analysis of Acts

The twins become blood brothers

Q1   When seven-year-old Mickey first appears, he is carrying a
toy gun. What does this suggest about the events to come?

....

....

Q2   How does Mrs Johnstone react when she realises that Mickey has
been near Edward's house? Use a quote to support your answer.

....

....

....

Q3   Why is Mickey surprised by Edward's generosity when they first meet?

....

....

Q4   Read from Edward's first line of the play until Mrs Johnstone sings the words
"On easy terms". Decide whether these statements are **true** or **false**.

	True	False
Mickey and Edward are eager to learn about each other's lives.	☐	☐
Mrs Johnstone and Mrs Lyons have both tried to keep the twins apart.	☐	☐
Edward thinks that Mickey is impressive.	☐	☐
Mrs Johnstone treats Edward lovingly when she finds him playing with Mickey.	☐	☐
Mrs Johnstone tries to tell Edward that she is his mother.	☐	☐

Q5   Read the scene where Edward goes home after meeting Mrs Johnstone for
the first time. Find a quote which backs up each of the following statements.

a) Edward has been influenced by his conversation with Mrs Johnstone.

....

b) Mrs Lyons is possessive of Edward.

....

The children get into trouble

Q1 Put these events in order by numbering the boxes. The first one has been done for you.

Mickey gets out Sammy's air pistol to show Linda. [1]

Edward gets into trouble with the Policeman. ☐

Edward leaves his garden to join Mickey and Linda. ☐

Mickey, Linda and Edward misbehave. ☐

Mickey and Linda lie about how they treat policemen. ☐

Mrs Lyons realises that Edward has disappeared. ☐

Q2 Answer each question and then choose a quote from the text that supports your answer.

a) How does Linda react when Sammy and his friends bully Mickey?

....

Quote: ....

b) How does Edward feel about the possibility of being caught by the police?

....

Quote: ....

c) What does Mr Lyons think about Mrs Lyons' concern over Edward's friendship with Mickey?

....

Quote: ....

Q3 Read from when Mrs Lyons says "**Oh Richard, Richard**" until the Narrator sings "**He's gonna find y'**". How does Russell show that Mrs Lyons' behaviour has changed since the start of the play?

....

....

Q4 How does Mickey feel when he realises that Linda is better at shooting than he is? Use an example to back up your answer.

....

....

....

Section One — Analysis of Acts

Both families move to Skelmersdale

Q1 How does the Policeman's visit affect Mr Lyons?

....

....

Q2 Read from when Mrs Lyons says "**Well, Edward... do you like it here?**" until Edward goes to read, then decide whether each statement is **true** or **false**. Find a short quote to support each answer.

a) Edward is anxious for his mother to be well again. **True:** ☐ **False:** ☐

Quote: ....

b) After the Lyonses have moved, Mickey no longer influences Edward. **True:** ☐ **False:** ☐

Quote: ....

Q3 How does Mrs Johnstone use the locket to strengthen the link between Mickey and Edward?

....

....

Q4 How does Russell hint that the Lyonses and the Johnstones have moved to the same place?

....

....

....

Q5 Mrs Johnstone thinks moving to Skelmersdale will improve her social standing. How does Russell show this? Use examples to reinforce your answer.

....

....

....

Trees, cows and a creepy magpie — the cure for all ills...

There's lots going on in Act One — you need to know what happens and which characters are involved. Choose three key events from Act One and write a sentence for each, explaining why it is important.

Section One — Analysis of Acts ☐ ☐ ☺ ☐

Act Two

Mickey and Edward get suspended from school

Q1 Read from the start of Act Two until Mrs Johnstone sings "**Not like Marilyn Monroe...**" Find an example to support each of the following statements.

   a) Mrs Johnstone's financial situation has improved since she moved to Skelmersdale.

   Example: ....

   b) Mrs Johnstone often worries about Edward.

   Example: ....

Q2 Read from when Mrs Lyons says "**One, two, three**" until the bus leaves. What similarities and differences are there between Edward and Mrs Lyons' scene and Mickey and Mrs Johnstone's?

© Donald Cooper/photostage

Similarities: ....

....

....

Differences: ....

....

....

Q3 How do you think Mrs Lyons feels about her life in Skelmersdale at the start of Act Two? Use a quote to support your answer.

....

....

Q4 Look at the scenes where the twins are at school. Read from when Mickey says "**Come on...**" until Edward says "**don't you have secrets?**" Using examples, answer the questions below.

   a) How does Russell use the school scenes to show that Edward and Mickey are similar?

   ....

   ....

   b) How does Mrs Lyons react when she sees the picture in the locket?

   ....

   ....

Section One — Analysis of Acts

The twins meet again as teenagers

Q1 Read the scene where Mickey and Linda are looking over the estate. Why do you think Linda tells Mickey that she thinks the boy in the window is "**lovely lookin'**"?

....

....

Q2 Read the scene where Mickey and Edward sing about being like "**That guy**". What does this song suggest about Mickey and Edward?

....

....

Q3 For each of the following moments from Act One, find an example of a similar event involving the same characters in Act Two.

Act One	Act Two
a) Mickey says "**Gis a sweet**" to Edward.	
b) Edward greets Mrs Johnstone very politely.	
c) Edward thinks Mrs Johnstone is "**smashing**".	

Q4 Read from when Edward meets Mrs Johnstone until the twins leave for the cinema. Explain how Mrs Johnstone's attitude towards Mickey and Edward's friendship has changed since Act One.

© Eric Richmond/ArenaPAL

....

....

....

....

....

Q5 Read the scene where Mrs Lyons attacks Mrs Johnstone with a knife. Explain how the events of this scene show that their relationship has changed since Act One.

....

....

....

Mickey and Edward become adults

Q1 Read the scene where Linda and the twins are confronted by the Policeman. How does Mickey and Linda's behaviour differ from when they meet the Policeman in Act One?

....

....

Q2 Read from when the Narrator says "**There's a few bob**" until he says "**just eighteen**", then answer the questions below.

    a) What does this extract suggest about Linda, Mickey and Edward's friendship?

    ....

    b) Why do you think Russell refers to "**broken bottles in the sand**"?

    ....

    ....

Q3 What does the audience learn about Edward when he sings to Linda before he leaves for university?

....

Q4 Why do you think Edward encourages Mickey to ask Linda to be his girlfriend?

....

....

Q5 Read from when Mrs Johnstone says "**Y' gonna be late, Mick**" until Mickey says "**Ta-ra, Mam**", then decide whether each statement is **true** or **false**. Find a short quote to support each answer.

    a) Mickey cares about what Mrs Johnstone thinks of him.   **True:** ☐   **False:** ☐

    Quote: ....

    b) Mrs Johnstone judges Mickey when she finds out Linda is pregnant.   **True:** ☐   **False:** ☐

    Quote: ....

    c) Mickey appreciates Mrs Johnstone.   **True:** ☐   **False:** ☐

    Quote: ....

The twins drift apart

Q1 Read the scene where Mr Lyons sings 'Miss Jones' until Edward offers Mickey money. Decide whether these statements are **true** or **false**.

	True	False

Mr Lyons is a caring employer.

Edward wants to introduce Mickey to his university friends.

Edward doesn't notice that Mickey is depressed about losing his job.

Mickey enjoyed his job in the factory.

Mickey struggles to find another job.

Q2 Mickey *"throws the notes to the ground"* when Edward offers him money. Why do you think he reacts so negatively to Edward's offer?

....

....

Q3 Read the scene where Edward proposes to Linda, then find a quote that shows Linda's feelings for Edward. Why do you think Russell reveals Linda's feelings for Edward at this point in the play?

Quote: ....

Explanation: ....

....

Q4 Read from when the Narrator says **"There's a full moon shining"** until Linda says **"Mickey, is that you?"** Explain how Russell links the events in this passage to earlier events in the play.

....

....

Q5 Explain what effect prison has on Mickey. Find a quote to support your answer.

Explanation: ....

....

....

Quote: ....

© Nils Jorgensen/REX/Shutterstock

Section One — Analysis of Acts

Mickey confronts Edward and the twins die

Q1 Read from when Mrs Johnstone sings "**With grace for good behaviour**" until she sings "**As the music ends**". Find a quote which supports the following statements.

a) Mrs Johnstone is worried about Mickey's welfare.

....

b) Linda thinks that Mickey's addiction has changed him.

....

c) Mrs Johnstone is understanding about Linda's affair with Edward.

....

Q2 Why do you think Mrs Lyons wants Mickey to know about Edward and Linda's relationship?

....

Q3 Read the scene where Mickey confronts Edward in the town hall.
How does Mickey treat Edward? Use a quote to support your answer.

....

....

....

Q4 What evidence is there that Mickey shoots Edward accidentally?

....

....

Q5 In the last song of the play, Mrs Johnstone struggles to accept that the twins have died.
Why do you think Russell ends the play in this way? Explain your answer.

....

....

....

 And here's a scene you saw earlier...

Making links between different parts of the play shows you know it well. Write a paragraph comparing Mickey and Edward's relationship when they are seven, fourteen, eighteen and in their early twenties.

      Section One — Analysis of Acts

Using Quotes

In the exam, you'll need to use quotes from the play to back up your argument. It's worth practising this skill because your answer will be much more convincing if you can give evidence for your views. You won't have the text with you in the exam, so you'll have to learn some important quotes off by heart. This page gives you the chance to think about how to choose good quotes and use them well — have a go at the questions below and you'll soon be well on your way to exam success.

Q1 Fill in the text about how to use quotes in your answers.

A good quote is .... — you should write your quote exactly as it appears

in the text. Good quotes are also highly .... to the point being made, so

don't choose something off topic. A bad quote will be ...., and won't

support the point you're discussing. A good quote will be .... in the

sentence, rather than just added on afterwards. Only use the most ....

part of a sentence or passage — it's easier to remember short quotes. Also, a quote

shouldn't just .... your point. It should give new information.

Q2 Look at these examples and decide which use quotes well and which use them badly.

a) Mickey has a good relationship with Mrs Johnstone. He tells her that the factory has "started layin' people off" and confides in her about Linda's pregnancy.

b) Mrs Lyons paints a picture of the luxurious lifestyle that she can afford to provide by claiming that her child would have "Silver trays" to eat from.

c) Linda and Mickey pretend that they say "dead funny things" to the police to impress Edward.

d) Mrs Johnstone thinks she'll have a new start in Skelmersdale — she thinks she'll be able to "begin again" once she moves away from Liverpool.

e) In Act Two, Mickey feels that he and Edward are not as close, telling him, "I grew up. An' you didn't, because you didn't need to; an' I don't blame y' for it, Eddie."

Good quote usage: ....   Bad quote usage: ....

Q3 Choose one of the examples you identified as bad in Q2 and improve it.

....

....

....

P.E.E.D.

To get a great mark, you have to do more than just comment on the text — your answer needs to be well-structured and developed. The P.E.E.D. method is a brilliant way to make sure you do this.

For each **point** you make in your answer, provide a supporting quote or a specific **example**, then **explain** how it backs up your point. Finally, **develop** your point by explaining the effect it has on the audience, or making a link with another part of the play, a different theme or the play's context.

Q1 None of the sample answers below have used P.E.E.D. correctly. For each, say which stage of P.E.E.D. is missing, then write a sentence you could include to improve the answer.

a)
> Mrs Lyons' paranoia causes her to lose control of her mind. In Act Two, after she attacks Mrs Johnstone, she accuses her of being a "Witch" and curses her. This contrasts with her firm belief in Act One that superstition is silly, which shows how fragile her mental state has become since the start of the play.

Missing stage: .... Addition: ....

....

....

b)
> Russell uses language related to superstition to create a threatening atmosphere. This superstitious imagery suggests that something bad will happen, creating an atmosphere of danger. The fact that the audience has already seen the tragic ending of the play makes the danger seem unavoidable, which heightens the sense of threat in this scene.

Missing stage: .... Addition: ....

....

....

c)
> Russell uses songs to change the mood of a scene. In Act One, he structures the play so that the final verse of 'Long Sunday Afternoon', which has a melancholy tone, is followed immediately by the opening line of 'Bright New Day'. The joyful and optimistic tone of 'Bright New Day' shatters the sad and thoughtful mood created by 'Long Sunday Afternoon'.

Missing stage: .... Addition: ....

....

....

   Section One — Analysis of Acts

Section Two — Characters

Mrs Johnstone

Q1 Find an example from Act One which supports each of the following statements.

    a) Mrs Johnstone tries to see the good in life.

    ....

    b) Mrs Johnstone sometimes acts without thinking about the consequences.

    ....

Q2 How does superstition affect Mrs Johnstone's life? Support your answer with an example.

    ....

    ....

    ....

Q3 Complete the table below to show what Mrs Johnstone's behaviour in Act Two suggests about her.

Event in the play	What it suggests about Mrs Johnstone
a) Mrs Johnstone refuses to leave Skelmersdale when Mrs Lyons tries to bribe her.	
b) Mrs Johnstone blames the teacher when Sammy burns the school down.	

Q4 At the start of the play, the Narrator says that Mrs Johnstone has **"a stone in place of her heart"**. Do you agree? Explain your answer.

© Eric Richmond/ArenaPAL

    ....

    ....

    ....

    ....

    ....

Ah, catalogues — the start of every good Christmas list...

Imagine you're Mrs Johnstone and you've just agreed to give a baby to Mrs Lyons. Write a short diary entry that explains why you decided to give one twin away and how you feel about the agreement.

Mr and Mrs Lyons

Q1 Decide whether these statements about Mrs Lyons are **true** or **false**.

	True	False
Mrs Lyons' aggressive nature is only revealed in Act Two.	☐	☐
Mrs Lyons takes advantage of her wealth and social position.	☐	☐
Mrs Lyons is prepared to hurt other people in order to keep Edward close to her.	☐	☐
Mrs Lyons becomes more fearful and insecure in Act Two.	☐	☐

Q2 Read from when Edward says "**Mummy, how do you spell bogey man?**" until Mrs Lyons says "**Oh my son...**" What impression of Mrs Lyons does the audience get in this extract?

....

....

....

Q3 Find a quote that shows that Mrs Lyons worries about her relationship with Edward. Explain how Mrs Lyons' insecurity influences the way that she treats Edward.

Quote: ....

Explanation: ....

....

Q4 Find a quote from the play that shows that Mr Lyons is:

a) patronising

Quote: ....

b) uninterested in family life

Quote: ....

© "Blood Brothers" Sydney 2015. Produced by Enda Markey. Photograph by Kurt Sneddon.

The Lyonses need to get themselves a decent shoe rack...

Write an essay plan for this question: **In what ways does Mrs Lyons change during the play?**
You should write about:
- how she reacts to Edward's relationship with the Johnstones
- the way she is presented in *Blood Brothers*.

Mickey Johnstone

Q1 Read from when Mickey meets Edward for the first time until he says
"**Ta ra, Eddie...**", then find a quote to back up each of these statements.

© Eric Richmond/ArenaPAL

a) Mickey doesn't trust other people's generosity.

Quote: ....

....

b) Mickey is sensitive.

Quote: ....

....

Q2 Find two examples in the text that show that Mickey lacks confidence as a fourteen-year-old.

1) ....

2) ....

Q3 Using examples, explain how Mickey's unemployment affects:

a) his state of mind

....

....

b) his attitude towards Edward

....

....

Q4 Read from when Mrs Lyons reveals Edward and Linda's affair until Mickey says "**I could have
been him!**" Using a quote, explain what Mickey's language suggests about how he is feeling.

....

....

....

PRACTICE TASK

Mickey wasn't so fine in the end...

Imagine that you're Edward and you've just met seven-year-old Mickey. Write down three adjectives
that you'd use to describe Mickey, then find an example from your first meeting to back up each one.

Section Two — Characters

Edward Lyons

Q1 Find a quote in Act One where Edward uses informal language when speaking with Mickey. What does this suggest about Edward?

Quote: ....

Explanation: ....

....

Q2 Find a quote from the play that shows that Edward is:

a) generous

Quote: ....

b) well mannered

Quote: ....

c) privileged

Quote: ....

© "Blood Brothers" Sydney 2015. Produced by Enda Markey. Photograph by Kurt Sneddon.

Q3 How does Russell suggest that Edward finds romantic relationships difficult in Act Two? Support your answer with an example from the play.

....

....

....

Q4 'Edward is a very loyal character'. Do you agree or disagree with this statement? Give reasons for your answer.

....

....

....

....

Section Two — Characters

Linda

Q1 Find a quote to back up each of these statements.

a) Linda acts bravely as a seven-year-old.

Quote: ....

b) Linda tries to be optimistic in Act One.

Quote: ....

c) As a teenager, Linda makes it obvious that she is fond of Mickey.

Quote: ....

Q2 Linda has a strong sense of humour as a child and a teenager.
Give an example of a time in each act when Russell shows this.

Act One: ....

Act Two: ....

Q3 How does Russell use the fairground scene to suggest that Linda's role in the play is changing?

....

....

....

....

Q4 Why do you think Linda has an affair with Edward?

....

....

....

....

MAKING LINKS

Linda was first in the queue for 'Swedish Au Pairs 2'...

Linda stands up to Sammy when he bullies Mickey in Act One. Write a few sentences making links between Linda's actions in this scene and the way she behaves in other similar scenes in the play.

Sammy Johnstone

Q1 Read from when Mickey recites "**I wish I was our Sammy**" to when Edward appears.
What does Russell show about the relationship between Sammy and Mickey in this passage?

....

....

....

Q2 Find a quote from Act One which supports each of the following statements.

a) Sammy judges people based on their social class.

....

b) Sammy enjoys the idea of violence.

....

c) Sammy acts as a leader when playing with others.

....

Q3 Sammy and Mickey both commit crime in the play. Explain why the audience might be less likely to forgive Sammy for his criminal behaviour than they would be to forgive Mickey.

© Elliott Franks/ArenaPAL

....

....

....

....

Q4 Read from when Sammy says "**We don't *use* the shooters**" until Mrs Johnstone sings
"**The jury found him guilty**". Why might Sammy be described as childlike in this extract?

....

....

 Sammy Johnstone! Step away from the magnesium...

PRACTICE TASK

Imagine you're writing a news article about Sammy after the petrol station robbery. Make a list of the events in Sammy's life that you would include to show how he gradually descends into a life of crime.

20

The Narrator

Q1 The Narrator becomes various minor characters, such as the Milkman, the Gynaecologist and the Teacher, during the play. Explain what this suggests about his character.

....

....

....

Q2 Read the scene where the Narrator sings the words "**Shoes upon the table**" after Mrs Johnstone is fired. What does the Narrator's language suggest about him? Support your answer with a quote.

....

....

....

Q3 Find an example in the text where the Narrator appears when another character is happy. Explain what effect this has on the mood of the scene.

Example: ....

....

Explanation: ....

....

Q4 How does Russell use stage directions to make the Narrator seem sinister? Use an example to back up your answer.

....

....

....

....

© "Blood Brothers" Sydney 2015. Produced by Enda Markey. Photograph by Kurt Sneddon.

The devil's gonna find y', after he's finished his tea...

If you're asked about the Narrator, you could write about how he drives the plot forward. In Act Two, he makes Linda and the twins' teenage years go by quickly by describing them during a montage.

Section Two — Characters

Making Links

A great way to develop your answer is to make links between your points and other parts of the text. For example, you could write about similar events, times when characters behave in a similar or different way or other times where a theme is presented. This page focuses on making links between various characters' actions, which will be a good recap of how Russell presents them at different times in the play. Have a look back through this section if you're in need of some inspiration.

Q1 Fill in the table below with examples to illustrate the key points about each character. You can either use quotes or just explain what happens, as long as it's a precise example.

Character	Key Point	Example One	Example Two
Mrs Johnstone	Mrs Johnstone is determined to build a better life for her family.		
Mickey	Mickey challenges those who have authority over him.		
Edward	Edward can be secretive.		

Q2 Now do the same for the characters below. This time, you'll need to think of your own key point about them.

Character	Key Point	Example One	Example Two
Linda			
Mrs Lyons			
Sammy			

Section Two — Characters

Practice Questions

Now that you're all caught up on who's who in the play, it's time to put your knowledge to the test and have a go at some practice questions. It's important not to rush this page — do the questions one at a time. It's worth spending about five minutes thinking about your answers and writing a plan for each one.

Q1 Explain the significance of the relationship between Edward and Mrs Johnstone in *Blood Brothers*.

You should write about:
- the nature of their relationship
- what this shows about each of their characters.

Q2 Explore how Russell presents the Narrator as a mysterious character in the play.

Q3 In what ways does Mickey change as the play progresses?

You should write about:
- how Russell presents Mickey in the play
- how Mickey is affected by the events in his life.

Q4 "**I must have my baby. We made an agreement, a bargain.**" (Mrs Lyons, Act One)

Explain the importance of the character of Mrs Lyons in the play.

Q5 Explore how Russell presents Mrs Johnstone as a victim in the play.

Liverpool in the Late Twentieth Century

Q1   Read the paragraph below and fill in the gaps.

The play is .... between the 1960s and the 1980s, which was a time of great

economic change in Britain. Traditional ...., like shipbuilding and mining,

were in decline. Liverpool was very badly hit by this decline because its ....

depended heavily on shipbuilding. Many people from the .... class there

became unemployed and had to rely on .... from the government.

Q2   High levels of unemployment in Liverpool in the late 1970s and 1980s contributed to an increase
in crime. Explain how this link between poverty and crime is shown through Mickey's character.

....

....

....

Q3   The areas where the Johnstones and the Lyonses live in Act One are very different, despite not
being far from each other. What does this suggest about Liverpool at the time the play was set?

....

....

Q4   In the late 20th century, many people in Liverpool were rehoused to 'New Towns' — redeveloped
areas with extra housing. Use this information and the play to answer the questions below.

a) These people often had no say in where they were rehoused. How does the play reflect this?

....

....

b) Some people saw being relocated to New Towns as a good opportunity.
How does Mrs Johnstone's attitude to Skelmersdale reflect this?

....

....

They say I'm not industrious, but I build paper planes...

Blood Brothers isn't just for entertainment — it has a social message too. Applying context to
themes and characters in the exam will help you to explore what Russell's message really is.

Money and Social Class

Q1 Write down two ways in which social class determines the course of Edward's life.

1) ....

2) ....

Q2 Decide whether these statements about social class in the play are **true** or **false**.

	True	False
Both middle-class and working-class characters display class prejudice.	☐	☐
Russell suggests that class differences matter more in adulthood than in childhood.	☐	☐
The play suggests that working-class people are lazy and immoral.	☐	☐
Society is shown to be very divided by class in the play.	☐	☐

Q3 Give an example of a time in the play when Mrs Lyons' social status gives her an advantage over Mrs Johnstone. Then explain how she uses this advantage to gain power over Mrs Johnstone.

Example: ....

Explanation: ....

....

Q4 The stage directions say that Mickey's school is "**all boredom and futility**". Why might Mickey and his school friends think their education is 'futile' (pointless)? Mention class in your answer.

....

....

....

....

© "Blood Brothers" Sydney 2015. Produced by Enda Markey. Photograph by Kurt Sneddon.

Q5 Read Act One, from "**And he was about to commit a serious crime**" to "**Goodnight, sir.**" What does the Policeman's behaviour in this passage reveal about his attitude to social class?

....

....

....

Section Three — Context and Themes

Q6 Read the part of the play when Edward returns from university. Explain how Mickey's lack of money forces him to grow up more quickly than Edward.

....

....

Q7 After he has been made redundant, Mickey says that he'd "**crawl back**" to his job "**for half the pay and double the hours**". How do these quotes create sympathy for Mickey's situation?

....

....

....

Q8 Find a quote from the play to support each of the following statements.

a) Edward doesn't appreciate how hard it is for Mickey to be unemployed.

Quote: ....

b) Mrs Johnstone's financial situation is insecure.

Quote: ....

c) Sammy uses the promise of money to persuade Mickey to be his lookout.

Quote: ....

Q9 In the play, middle-class characters often use money to try to solve their problems.

a) Find an example of a time in the play when Edward tries to do this.

....

b) In Act Two, Mrs Johnstone rejects Mrs Lyons' attempt to bribe her to move away from Skelmersdale. Do you think Mrs Lyons was expecting this reaction? Explain your answer.

....

....

....

Mickensian or Edwardian Britain? I know which I prefer...

Mrs Johnstone and Mrs Lyons are class stereotypes. Think about how the way Russell presents them links to the ideas about social class that might have been held by an audience in the early 1980s.

Section Three — Context and Themes

Fate and Superstition

Q1 Why do you think Russell shows the audience Mickey and Edward's fates at the start of the play?

....

....

Q2 The Narrator says "**the devil's got your number**" several times in the play, but it's sometimes unclear who he's speaking to. Give an example of a time when this happens, and then explain what effect it has.

© REX/Shutterstock

Example: ....

....

Explanation: ....

....

Q3 Read Act Two from when fourteen-year-old Mickey and Edward are reunited after 'That Guy' until Mickey says "**I know.**" How does this passage show that fate is a powerful force in the play?

....

....

....

Q4 Read the paragraph below and fill in the gaps.

The .... plays an important role in exploring ideas about fate. At the start of the

play, he tells the .... that the .... will die. His references to the

devil and to a "**debt**" that must be paid constantly .... the audience that the twins'

.... are approaching. This makes it seem as if their fate is ....

Q5 As Mrs Lyons becomes more afraid of losing Edward to the Johnstones, she tries harder to stop it from happening. What does this suggest about her belief in fate?

....

....

Section Three — Context and Themes

Q6 In the play, there are lots of references to superstitions that are related to bad luck. What effect does this have on the audience?

....

....

Q7 In Act One, Mrs Lyons invents a superstition that if the twins ever learn the truth, they'll both die. What does Mrs Johnstone's reaction to this suggest about the power of superstition?

....

....

....

Q8 Read Act One from "**He turns to look at her**" to "**the scene snaps from Mrs Lyons to the children**". How do the stage directions emphasise Mrs Lyons' fear of the shoes being on the table?

....

....

....

Q9 Russell doesn't make it clear what is to blame for the twins' deaths. Some different options are listed in the table below. Complete the table by filling in the gaps.

What's to blame?	Argument for	Argument against
a) Class	Class becomes the main source of conflict between the twins at the end of the play.	Even though class influences the characters' behaviour, the characters are still responsible for their own actions.
b) Superstition		
c) Fate		

The Devil hasn't got my number — I swapped networks...

PRACTICE TASK

Write an essay plan for the following question: **Explain how the theme of fate is significant in the play.** Think about the way fate is presented and the role fate plays in *Blood Brothers* as a whole.

28

Childhood and Growing Up

Q1 Give two ways in which Mickey's experience of childhood is different to Edward's.

1) ....

2) ....

Q2 Russell presents childhood as a time of innocence.
How does this make the rest of the play seem more tragic?

....

....

....

© "Blood Brothers" Sydney 2015. Produced by Enda Markey. Photograph by Kurt Sneddon.

Q3 In the 1960s and 1970s, popular culture became more developed in Britain. Music, television and films had a big influence on children. How is this reflected in the play? Give one example.

....

....

Q4 Find a quote to support the following statements.

a) Edward doesn't have many opportunities to spend time with girls.

Quote: ....

b) Mickey doesn't know how to tell Linda how he feels about her.

Quote: ....

Q5 The play shows that growing up is linked to gaining more responsibility.
How is this emphasised by the contrast between Mickey and Edward in Act Two?

....

....

....

Worm funerals — the things you miss out on as an adult...

Growing up is hard for Russell's characters — Mickey in particular faces a lot of pressure as a young adult. If you're writing about this in the exam, think about how it affects his relationships with others.

Friendship

Q1 Read the scene where Mickey and Edward become blood brothers, from when Mickey says **"'Ey, we were born on the same day"** until Edward says **"And stand by him."**

    a) How does Russell suggest that Mickey has power over Edward in this passage?

    ....

    ....

    b) Explain how the balance of power between the twins has changed by the end of the play.

    ....

    ....

Q2 Edward's friendship with Mickey and Linda gives him a sense of belonging.
Why do you think this sense of belonging is so important to Edward when he's a child?

....

....

....

....

Q3 In Act One, Russell shows the admiration the twins have for each other through the song 'My Friend'. Find a quote from Act Two which shows that this attitude changes.

....

Q4 Adult friendships seem more complicated than childhood friendships in the play.
How does Russell use the relationship between Linda and the twins to show this?

....

....

....

Edward's my BFF — my Back-stabbing Fancy Friend...

Make a spider diagram about the twins' friendship. Draw a branch for Mrs Johnstone, Mrs Lyons and Linda, then jot down the ways in which each of them influences Mickey and Edward's relationship.

Identity

Q1 Mickey and Edward are twins. How does this allow Russell to explore ideas about upbringing and identity?

....

....

Q2 Decide whether these statements are **true** or **false**.

	True	False
The twins seem to be naturally drawn to each other.	☐	☐
Although Mrs Lyons brings Edward up, she doesn't feel like he's her son.	☐	☐
Mickey and Edward have identical personalities.	☐	☐
Mickey's behaviour is usually very similar to Sammy's.	☐	☐

Q3 Edward has a very privileged childhood. Give one way that this is shown to shape his personality. Use a quote to support your answer.

....

....

Q4 Read the duet 'My Child' in Act One, then read the duet 'That Guy' in Act Two. These songs have the same melody. Why do you think this is? Write about identity in your answer.

....

....

Q5 At the end of the play, Mickey asks Mrs Johnstone why she didn't give him away instead, claiming he "**could have been**" Edward. Do you think this is true? Explain your answer.

....

....

....

....

I'd be pretty miffed too if I found out I had a secret twin...

Write about the importance of the theme of identity in *Blood Brothers*. You should discuss the different ideas about identity that appear in the play and how identity influences the play overall.

Section Three — Context and Themes

Gender

Q1 Read the paragraph below and fill in the gaps.

In the late 20th century, men and women still had very ....

roles. Women were expected to look after the .... and children,

while men were expected to .... to provide money for the

.... This is the case with the Lyons family, and with the family

.... and .... have when they've grown up.

Q2 Describe how Mrs Johnstone's family role is different to the traditional family role of a woman in the 1960s and 1970s.

....

....

Q3 How might Mrs Lyons' desperation to be a mother reflect traditional gender roles of the time? Write about the play's context in your answer.

....

....

....

Q4 By the end of the play, Linda is leading a very similar lifestyle to Mrs Johnstone. What message do you think Russell gets across to the audience by creating this similarity between them?

....

....

Q5 Mr Lyons doesn't spend much time at home but he works hard. Do you think this would have made him seem like a good father to an audience in the 1980s? Give a reason for your answer.

....

....

PRACTICE TASK

I don't care for gendered rolls — I eat all types of bread...

Write a couple of paragraphs explaining how the events of the play might have been different if Mrs Johnstone's husband hadn't left her. Make sure you include what might have happened instead.

Writing about Context

To get a high mark in the exam, you have to know about the play's context. *Blood Brothers* is set in Liverpool between the 1960s and the 1980s, so you need to have an understanding of what society was like during this period, and which important historical events affected life in the UK around then. Adding contextual information and linking it to the key themes will help you improve your answer. The questions on this page will get you thinking about context and how to use it in your responses.

Q1 Read the sample answer extracts below and underline the contextual information.

> **a)** Russell uses the song 'Miss Jones' to create sympathy for the working class. Mr Lyons tells Miss Jones that despite her "years of splendid service, / Et cetera blah blah blah", he is making her redundant. The way that Mr Lyons reduces his employee's years of service to meaningless words makes him seem heartless, creating sympathy for Miss Jones. Her sudden redundancy reflects the fact that the widespread unemployment caused by the decline of traditional industries in the 1970s and 1980s affected the working class particularly badly. Russell's use of the name "Jones", one of the most common British surnames, shows his desire to create sympathy for the class as a whole, as it implies that Miss Jones' situation is not unique and could apply to any worker in the country.

> **b)** The similarity between Mrs Johnstone and her daughter Donna Marie is used to show the fixed role that many women in Britain had in the second half of the 20th century. In Act Two, Mrs Johnstone reveals that Donna Marie already has three children, claiming that she's "A bit like me that way". This likeness shows that Donna Marie has grown up to occupy the same restrictive maternal role as her mother. In the 1960s and 1970s, many people believed that a woman's role was to have children and look after the household. By showing that this role is passed on to the next generation in the play, Russell reflects the fact that this view was very firmly rooted in British society at the time.

Q2 Write down a piece of context that could be included in the sample answer below.

> Explore how class divides are presented in *Blood Brothers*.

> In the play, Russell uses the characters of Mickey and Edward to explore the effect of class divides. Their different experiences are highlighted when Edward returns from university. Mickey is resentful that Edward can still be "a kid", while he has been forced to grow up.

....

....

....

....

Practice Questions

Russell's play deals with a lot of different themes, from social class to friendship. It's important to understand how each theme is presented and how it's significant to the play as a whole, so here are some practice questions to help you check how much has sunk in. Include relevant context in your answers too.

Q1 **"We were friends, weren't we? Blood brothers, wasn't it?"** (Mickey, Act Two)

How are the characters of Mickey and Edward used by Russell in the play to explore ideas about friendship?

Q2 How is the theme of childhood significant in the play?

Q3 How are characters used to explore ideas about superstition in the play?

You should write about:
- different ideas about superstition that are presented in the play
- how these are explored through different characters.

Q4 Explore how working-class life is presented in the play.

Q5 **"I love the bones of every one of them."** (Mrs Johnstone, Act One)

Explain how Mrs Johnstone is presented as a motherly figure in *Blood Brothers*.

Section Three — Context and Themes

Section Four — The Writer's Techniques

Structure in 'Blood Brothers'

Q1 The play has a cyclical structure — the start is very similar to the end. What is the effect of this?

....

Q2 Find an example of a place in Act One where Russell uses a time jump, then explain its effect.

Example: ....

....

Effect: ....

....

Q3 Read the montage in Act Two where Linda, Mickey and Edward age from fifteen to eighteen, then answer the questions below.

a) Explain how this montage affects the pace of the play.

....

b) Why do you think Russell shows the characters ageing on stage instead of using a time jump?

....

....

Q4 How does Russell create dramatic irony when the twins become blood brothers? Explain the effect of this irony.

Dramatic irony is when the audience knows something that the characters on stage don't know.

....

....

Q5 Read the scenes in Act One where Mrs Johnstone and Mrs Lyons find out that the twins are friends. Why do you think Russell shows their reactions to this news in consecutive scenes?

....

....

....

This play should come with a massive spoiler warning...

Write about the importance of structure in *Blood Brothers*. Write about the ways in which Russell structures the play and how he uses structure to explore key themes. Make a plan before you start.

Form in 'Blood Brothers'

Q1 *Blood Brothers* has some features of a classical tragedy. In many classical tragedies, a chorus comments on the play's events. How does Russell adapt this aspect of the tragic form in his play?

....

....

....

Q2 In classical tragedies, the main character is often destroyed by their 'fatal flaw' — the biggest fault in their personality. Why do you think Russell chooses not to give his central characters a fatal flaw?

© Donald Cooper/photostage

....

....

....

....

....

Q3 The song 'That Guy' acts like a soliloquy. What effect does this have on the audience?

A soliloquy is a speech in which a character thinks out loud about their emotions. It's not directed at any other characters.

....

....

Q4 In some ways, *Blood Brothers* is similar to a cautionary fairy tale. Complete the table to show how the following features of cautionary fairy tales are reflected in *Blood Brothers*.

Feature of cautionary fairy tales	How it is reflected in *Blood Brothers*
a) They contain a moral warning or message for the audience.	
b) They are often told in rhyme.	

A roast dinner without gravy — now that's a tragedy...

Russell uses songs and lyrics to help convey messages in *Blood Brothers*. Choose two different songs and write a couple of sentences explaining how each one highlights an important idea in the play.

Section Four — The Writer's Techniques

Language in 'Blood Brothers'

Q1 Read the scene where the Johnstones sing 'Bright New Day' at the end of Act One. How does the Johnstones' language make this scene realistic? Support your answer with an example.

....

....

Q2 In Act One, the Narrator says "**An' did y' never hear of the mother, so cruel**". How does his speech in this line differ from his language in the rest of the scene?

....

....

....

....

© Ray Tang/REX/Shutterstock

Q3 Complete the table below to show the effect of these language techniques.

Technique	Example	Effect
	The Narrator says the line "**Someone broke the lookin' glass**" in two different scenes. (Act One)	
Rhyme	Sammy chants "**You're dead / Y' know y' are / I got y' standin' / Near that car.**" (Act One)	
Metaphor		

Q4 Read the scene in Act Two where Mrs Lyons accuses Mrs Johnstone of following her. How does Russell use language to reflect Mrs Lyons' fragile state of mind?

....

....

....

Atmosphere and Mood

Q1   Read the scene in Act One where Mrs Lyons and Mrs Johnstone
make their agreement. How does Russell create an uneasy
atmosphere in this scene? Support your answer with a quote.

....

....

....

Q2   Give an example of a moment in the play where the mood is:

optimistic ....

humorous ....

sad ....

Q3   Read the scene in Act One where Mrs Lyons realises that Edward has gone missing. How does
the Narrator create a menacing atmosphere in this scene? Support your answer with a quote.

....

....

....

....

Q4   How does Russell create a sense of panic when Mickey is searching for
Edward at the end of Act Two? Use an example to support your answer.

....

....

....

....

The Narrator brings atmos-fear wherever he goes...

Find an example of a scene in Act Two where the mood of the play changes suddenly. Write a few
sentences that explain how the mood changes and what techniques Russell uses to create this effect.

38

Imagery and Symbolism

Q1 Read Mrs Johnstone's first song in Act One, then answer the questions below.

    a) Give one motif which is used to symbolise happiness in this song.   A motif is a recurring symbol.

....

    b) Read the scene where Mickey is sent to prison. How has the meaning behind this motif changed since Act One? Find a quote to support your answer.

Explanation: ....

....

Quote: ....

Q2 Read from when Mrs Lyons puts the shoes on the table until just before the Gynaecologist enters. How does Russell use imagery of superstition in this scene?

....

....

Q3 How does Russell show that the twins becoming blood brothers is a symbolic moment?

....

....

....

© "Blood Brothers" Sydney 2015. Produced by Enda Markey. Photograph by Kurt Sneddon.

Q4 How does Russell use imagery associated with the weather to symbolise Linda and Mickey's loss of freedom and innocence in Act Two? Use an example to support your answer.

....

....

....

....

I just met a wizard optician. He's an expert in I-magery...

Russell uses motifs to foreshadow important events in the play. For example, the motif of guns is used to link Sammy and Mickey's games in Act One with their robbery of the petrol station in Act Two.

Section Four — The Writer's Techniques

'Blood Brothers' on the Stage

Q1 The same actors play each role throughout the play.
Explain what effect this has in the following scenes.

a) The scene where Linda, Sammy and Mickey play "*goodies and baddies*". (Act One)

....

....

b) The scene where Mickey and Linda argue after Mickey leaves prison. (Act Two)

....

....

Q2 Fill in the table below to show how Russell uses stage directions to describe background music and explain the effect of this music on the scene.

Moment in play	Stage direction	Effect of music
a) Mickey and Edward say goodbye when Edward moves away. (Act One)		
b) Mrs Lyons attacks Mrs Johnstone in her kitchen. (Act Two)		

Q3 In *Blood Brothers*, it is implied that the Johnstones' and the Lyonses' houses are positioned on opposite sides of the stage. What effect does this layout have on the audience?

....

....

Q4 The scenes that take place outside or away from the twins' houses are staged in an open space between the two houses. Why do you think Russell does this?

....

....

Russell's staging techniques made quite a scene...

If you're writing about class differences, think about how the twins' costumes reflect stereotypes about social class — Mickey is often dressed untidily while Edward usually wears smart, expensive clothing.

Staging and Dramatic Techniques

Blood Brothers was written to be performed, so it's important to be familiar with the staging and dramatic techniques that Russell uses. On this page you'll practise writing about these aspects of the play. You can quote stage directions in the same way as dialogue to give evidence for your points.

Don't forget to think about the P.E.E.D. structure (see pages 13 and 45 for more on this) — it'll help you to remember to give examples and think about the effects that Russell creates in the play.

Q1 Read Act Two of *Blood Brothers* from when Mrs Lyons "***points out***" Edward and Linda until Mrs Johnstone "***walks down the centre aisle***". Find stage directions which demonstrate the following points and briefly explain them. Use the example below to help you.

Mickey becomes angry with Linda when he learns of the affair.

After learning of the affair, Mickey starts "*hammering*" on his door while shouting for Linda — his "*hammering*" makes him seem physically aggressive.

a) Edward holds a powerful position as Councillor.

....

....

b) Mickey and Edward are uncertain around each other.

....

....

Q2 When Mickey goes into the Lyonses' house in Act One, he is "***pursued***" by Mrs Lyons, who "***ushers***" him out. How do these stage directions add to Russell's presentation of Mrs Lyons?

....

....

....

Q3 Find three stage directions in Act One which show how the actor playing Edward should deliver his lines. What do they tell you about Edward as a character?

Stage directions: ....

Explanation: ....

....

....

Section Four — The Writer's Techniques

Practice Questions

After all that drama, it's time for a change of scene with some classic practice exam questions. Include points about the different techniques Russell uses in the play to see how well this section has sunk in. Remember to scribble a quick plan for each question before you start, just like you would in the exam.

Q1   Write about how the settings are presented in *Blood Brothers*.

You should write about:
- the nature of the set and its effects
- how Russell uses different locations in the play to convey important ideas.

Q2   **"But y' know the devil's got your number, / Y' know he's gonna find y'"**
(The Narrator, Act One)

Explore how Russell creates tension in *Blood Brothers*.

Q3   How are class differences presented in *Blood Brothers*?

Q4   **"Wherever I go you'll be just behind me. I know that now... always and for ever and ever like, like a shadow"** (Mrs Lyons, Act Two)

How is the conflict between Mrs Johnstone and Mrs Lyons presented in the play?

Q5   Write about Russell's use of atmosphere in *Blood Brothers*.

You should write about:
- how Russell creates atmosphere in the play
- how Russell uses atmosphere to convey important ideas.

Understanding the Question

Underline key words in the question

Q1 Underline the most important words in the following questions. The first one has been done for you.

a) <u>Explain</u> <u>how</u> Russell <u>presents</u> the theme of <u>identity</u> in the play.

b) Explain the significance of Edward in *Blood Brothers*.

c) Explain how the theme of fate is explored in *Blood Brothers*.

d) How is staging used to create tension in *Blood Brothers*?

e) Explain how the importance of class division is explored in the play.

f) How is the character of Mickey presented in *Blood Brothers*?

g) Explain why Linda changes in the play.

Make sure you understand exam language

Q2 Match each exam question to the correct explanation of what you would need to do to answer it. You'll only need to use each white box once.

a) Explain how Russell presents the theme of identity in the play.	**1)** Analyse how a character contributes to the action and overall message of the play.
b) Explain the significance of Edward in *Blood Brothers*.	**2)** Analyse how Russell writes about a character.
c) Explain how the importance of class division is explored in the play.	**3)** Analyse the reasons for a development or event in the text.
d) How is the character of Mickey presented in *Blood Brothers*?	**4)** Analyse how a theme contributes to the action and overall message of the play.
e) Explain why Linda changes in the play.	**5)** Analyse how Russell writes about a theme in the play.

Exam language — mainly just sighs of despair...

No matter how keen you might be to start your essay, make sure you read the question several times and think about exactly what you're being asked to do. You don't want to end up writing about the wrong thing...

Making a Rough Plan

Jot down your main ideas

Q1 Look at the exam question below, then complete the spider diagram with at least three more main points for answering it.

Don't forget to underline the key words in the question before you start.

Linda and the twins' friendship becomes more complicated when they grow up.

How is the theme of friendship explored in *Blood Brothers*?

Put your best points and examples in a logical order

Q2 Choose your three best points from Q1 and fill in the plan below, adding evidence (a quote or an example from the play) for each point.

(Introduction)

Point One: ....

Evidence: ....

Point Two: ....

Evidence: ....

Point Three: ....

Evidence: ....

(Conclusion)

Don't jump to conclusions — plan your essay carefully...

A plan is your friend. It'll help you stay focused under pressure, stop you going off track and reassure you if you start to panic. And it only takes five minutes of your time — I'm sure you can spare that for such a good friend...

Section Five — Exam Buster

Making Links

Make links with other parts of the text

Q1 Look at the exam question and the table below. Complete the table with other relevant parts of the text which could be used to back up each point.

> Write about how Russell explores ideas about upbringing in *Blood Brothers*.

Point	Example 1	Example 2
Mickey and Sammy are very different despite having the same upbringing.	Mickey accepts Edward but Sammy is prejudiced against him.	
Mickey experiences prejudice because of his upbringing.	The Policeman treats Mickey severely because he is related to Sammy.	
Edward's good manners highlight his middle-class upbringing.	Mrs Johnstone is surprised when seven-year-old Edward asks her how she is.	

Extend your essay with other examples

You won't have time to do really detailed planning in the exam so you should get into the habit of quickly thinking of links when you're doing practice questions.

Q2 Look back at the points you included in your plan in Q2 on p.43. For each point, write down another example from a different part of the text that you could include in your essay.

Example for Point One: ....

....

Example for Point Two: ....

....

Example for Point Three: ....

....

If you liked this page, you may also like page 21...

Finding links between different parts of the text will make your answer more convincing and show that you have a solid understanding of the play. It's a lot easier to do this if you're really familiar with the text, so get reading...

Structuring Your Answer

P.E.E.D. stands for Point, Example, Explain, Develop

Q1 Read the following extract from an exam answer. Label each aspect of P.E.E.D.

> Russell suggests that a person's upbringing can't erase their natural identity. For example, Mrs Lyons wants to move away from Liverpool because she thinks that Edward is "drawn to" the Johnstones. This highlights her concern that his natural identity will prove stronger than the middle-class upbringing that she has tried to give him. Russell reinforces the idea that Edward's natural identity is still intact by highlighting similarities between the twins throughout the play.

Embedding quotes is a great way to give evidence

Q2 Rewrite the following sentences so that a short part of the quote is embedded in each one.

a) Edward thinks that misbehaving would be amusing. — "Oh, that sounds like super fun."

....

b) Mickey thinks that Edward is immature. — "But I suppose you still are a kid, aren't ye?"

....

Structure your answer using the P.E.E.D. method

Q3 Use the P.E.E.D. method to structure a paragraph on your first point from Q2 on page 43.

Point: ....

....

Example: ....

....

Explain: ....

....

Develop: ....

....

Surely you didn't think I'd stoop that low...

This is a serious and important topic in a serious and important publication — it's no place for toilet humour. (Tee hee.) Using the P.E.E.D. method will make sure your paragraphs are beautifully clear and structured.

Section Five — Exam Buster

Introductions and Conclusions

Give a clear answer to the question in your introduction

Q1 Read the question and the introduction extracts below. Decide which is better and explain why.

> How are Mickey and Edward used to present ideas about fate in the play?

a)
> Fate is a significant theme in *Blood Brothers*. The theme is presented using several characters, including Mickey, Edward and the Narrator. For example, at the end of the play, the Narrator asks whether "superstition" was to blame. As well as this, the way that Mickey and Edward keep meeting each other highlights how strong their friendship is.

b)
> Mickey and Edward are central to Russell's presentation of ideas about fate. They are used to suggest that people have a destiny that controls their lives. The twins' deaths are revealed to the audience in the opening moments of the play, creating the impression that Mickey and Edward are unable to escape their fate.

Better intro: .... Reason: ....

....

....

....

Don't write any new points in your conclusion

Q2 Read the conclusion to the exam question in Q1, then say how it could be improved.

> In conclusion, Mickey and Edward have a strong bond that can't be broken. Mickey and Edward have a tragic destiny, so they're used to explore the power of fate. In addition, Mrs Lyons' attempts to separate Edward from Mickey are ineffective.

....

....

....

....

....

I find introductions tricky — I'm terrible with names...

Have a go at writing an introduction and a conclusion for the exam question on p.43. Keep in mind the good and bad examples you've looked at on this page and make sure what you write is relevant to your main points.

Writing about Context

Make sure you can link the play to its context

Q1 Match each event with the relevant contextual information.

a) Mickey and Edward argue about money and opportunities after Mickey loses his job.

b) As a single mother, Mrs Johnstone is forced to find employment outside the family home.

c) Mr Lyons fires several employees and his secretary but manages to keep his own job.

1) The economic downturn of the 1970s and 1980s had a particularly severe impact on working-class people.

2) Children who attended private school in the late 20th century often went on to university instead of having to earn a wage.

3) In the late 20th century, men were generally expected to provide for their families.

Include context in your answer

Q2 Read the sample answer below and underline the contextual information.
Then write a paragraph using your second point from page 43 and
include contextual information of your own. Use the P.E.E.D. method.

> Russell uses the twins to highlight the power of fate over people's lives. Mrs Lyons tries to separate the twins by moving to Skelmersdale, but her plan fails when the Johnstones are rehoused there. The fact that the Johnstones are moved to the town where the Lyonses live is significant, as families who were moved to New Towns like Skelmersdale in the 1960s had no control over where they were sent. This suggests that fate is working to bring Mickey and Edward together. Russell uses this to suggest to the audience that fate is so powerful that it can't be changed or avoided.

....

....

....

....

....

....

I sent my mate a joke message — he really fell for my con-text...

You'll impress the examiner if you can make links between events in the play and its context. For example, one way to do this is by writing about how the social expectations of the time influence the characters' behaviour.

Linking Ideas and Paragraphs

Link your ideas so your argument is easy to follow

Q1   Rewrite the sample answer below, adding words and/or phrases so the ideas are clearly linked.

> In the play, Edward often forgets how privileged he is. In Act Two, Edward asks Mickey "why is a job so important?" Edward struggles to understand what life is like for Mickey, as he has never experienced poverty. Edward and Mickey's relationship breaks down when he tries to give Mickey money.

....

....

....

....

....

Q2   Write a paragraph using your third point from p.43. Make sure your ideas are properly connected.

....

....

....

....

....

Show how your paragraphs follow on from each other

Q3   Look at the three paragraphs you have written on pages 45, 47 and in Q2 on this page. Write down linking words or phrases you could use to link them together in your answer.

Paragraphs to link	Linking word or phrase
p.45 and p.47	
p.47 and p.48	

Click on this <u>link</u> for guaranteed exam success...*

No one is trying to catch you out in the exam, so don't panic. Make sure you read the question carefully and please, *please* spend five minutes planning — it'll help you no end.

Marking Answer Extracts

Get familiar with the mark scheme

Grade band	An answer at this level...
8-9	• shows an insightful and critical personal response to the text • closely and perceptively analyses how the writer uses language, form and structure to create meaning and affect the reader, making use of highly relevant subject terminology • supports arguments with well-integrated, highly relevant and precise examples from the text • gives a detailed exploration of the relationship between the text and its context • uses highly varied vocabulary and sentence types, with mostly accurate spelling and punctuation
6-7	• shows a critical and observant personal response to the text • includes a thorough exploration of how the writer uses language, form and structure to create meaning and affect the reader, making use of appropriate subject terminology • supports arguments with integrated, well-chosen examples from the text • explores the relationship between the text and its context • uses a substantial range of vocabulary and sentence types, with generally accurate spelling and punctuation
4-5	• shows a thoughtful and clear personal response to the text • examines how the writer uses language, form and structure to create meaning and affect the reader, making some use of relevant subject terminology • integrates appropriate examples from the text • shows an understanding of contextual factors • uses a moderate range of vocabulary and sentence types, without spelling and punctuation errors which make the meaning unclear

Have a go at marking an answer extract

Q1   Using the mark scheme, put the sample answer extract below in a grade band and explain why.

> How is Mrs Lyons presented as an unpleasant character in *Blood Brothers*?

> Russel presents Mrs Lyons as unpleasant in the play. He does this by showing that she goes back on her promises. For example, she fired Mrs Johnstone even though shes told her she can see Edward "every day". This shows that she is dishonest and unpleasant. In the 20th century, employers like Mrs Lyons had lots of power over people like Mrs Johnston. Mrs Lyons seems even more unpleasant in contrast to Mrs Johnstone, who is a nicer character.

Grade band: ....   Reason: ....

....

....

....

Marking Answer Extracts

Have a look at these extracts from answers to the question on page 49

Q1 For each extract, say what grade band you think it is in, then underline an example of where it meets each of the mark scheme criteria. Label each underlined point to show what it achieves.

---

a) Russell uses stage directions to present Mrs Lyons as an aggressive character. In Act One, she hits Edward *"hard and instinctively"* when he swears. The word *"instinctively"* suggests that she uses violence without thinking, implying that she is a naturally aggressive person. This emphasises her unpleasant nature to the audience. In Act Two, Mrs Lyons attacks Mrs Johnstone with a knife *"On impulse"*, which suggests that her aggressive instincts have become more powerful, making her seem more violent and out of control.

Similarly, Mrs Lyons is presented as increasingly manipulative through the way she uses her social position. In the song 'My Child', Mrs Johnstone and Mrs Lyons complete each other's rhymes, which suggests that they are united in building the same dream for Mrs Johnstone's baby. This makes Mrs Lyons seem encouraging, rather than manipulative. However, shortly afterwards, Mrs Lyons uses the untruthful accusation "You sold your baby" to exploit Mrs Johnstone's fear that the authorities will be biased against her. Later in the play, the Policeman treats Mrs Johnstone more harshly than Mr Lyons when their sons have behaved in the same way, highlighting the class prejudice that was common in Britain in the 1960s and 1970s. The fact that Mrs Johnstone's mistrust of the authorities is well-founded makes Mrs Lyons' behaviour seem even more manipulative to the audience.

Grade band: ....

---

b) Mrs Lyons' treatment of Mrs Johnstone reveals her lack of empathy. When Mrs Johnstone is upset in Act One, Mrs Lyons appears concerned and says "Why don't you sit down". However, she quickly becomes controlling when she thinks she will gain a child, saying "Give one to me" and scaring Mrs Johnstone with threats about social services taking away her children. The structure of this scene highlights Mrs Lyons' sudden change in attitude, as her concern is quickly replaced by repeated commands and heavy persuasion. This suggests that her concern for Mrs Johnstone was not real, revealing her lack of empathy. This hints to the audience that the positive impression of Mrs Lyons that Russell has given so far doesn't show her true nature.

Mrs Lyons is shown to be judgemental through her attitude towards Mickey. When Edward brings Mickey to his house in Act One, Mrs Lyons asks him "Do you go to the same school as Edward?" This focus on Mickey's school gives the impression that Mrs Lyons is questioning him about his background. This makes her seem judgemental by highlighting her class prejudice towards Mickey. Her judgemental nature is reinforced later in the scene when she encourages Edward to think that the Johnstones and the Lyonses are different, showing that she approves of the strong class divides that existed in the late 20th century.

Grade band: ....

Marking a Whole Answer

Q1 Read the sample answer below. On page 52, put it in a grade band and explain your decision.

> How is the theme of gender presented in *Blood Brothers*?

If it helps you, label examples of where the answer meets the mark scheme criteria.

In *Blood Brothers*, Russell presents gender as a limiting factor for women living in patriarchal (male-dominated) societies. He does this by exploring the relationships between Mr and Mrs Johnstone and Mr and Mrs Lyons. He also shows the gender roles which were influential in the late 20th century to be oppressive through various characters, including Mickey, who is used to suggest that men can also suffer as a result of their gender. Moreover, Russell shows that gender roles are learned, not natural, by demonstrating that children are not affected by them. This suggests that gender expectations play a significant role in determining the way that people are treated in society.

Russell uses staging and structure to present the way that women suffer in male-dominated societies. Immediately after the twins' birth, various debt collectors arrive to demand money from Mrs Johnstone. Their presence on stage at the same time shows that she faces multiple financial pressures, while the fact that they appear straight after she gives birth suggests that she has no relief from these pressures. Men were expected to provide for their families at the time the play is set, so Mrs Johnstone's struggle highlights the impact of her husband's abandonment. At the start of the play, the Narrator's suggestion that the audience judge how Mrs Johnstone "came to play this part" of a mother of dead sons is followed by her line "Once I had a husband". This transition suggests that the tragic outcome of the play can be traced back to Mr Johnstone's abandonment of his family, reinforcing the idea that single mothers struggle to thrive in patriarchal societies because of their gender.

Russell also presents the gender roles common in traditional families as divisive. In Act One, Mr Lyons tells Mrs Lyons that the home is her "domain". The word "domain" implies that Mrs Lyons has a specific area of power but also that this power has boundaries. The idea that her role is to care for the home, while Mr Lyons' role is to provide for the family, is consistent with the gender roles that were common in the late 20th century. However, the fact that Mr Lyons gives Mrs Lyons her "domain" and makes important decisions relating to it, such as whether the family should move house, shows that he is still ultimately in charge. This suggests that the roles that women are expected to fulfil are defined by men. Russell therefore uses Mr and Mrs Lyons to reflect the inequality between men and women in the late 20th century.

Russell develops the idea that women are disadvantaged by their gender by suggesting that their gender limits their power more than their class does. He structures the play to highlight how Mrs Lyons' power over Mrs Johnstone actually depends on her husband. In Act One, Mrs Lyons says that "we both think it would be better if you left" and "we're not satisfied". The repetition of the plural "we", instead of the singular 'I', suggests that the Lyonses are united in their opposition to Mrs Johnstone, which makes Mrs Lyons seem more powerful. However, the audience has already seen that Mr Lyons gives his wife the money she uses in her bribery. This implies that Mrs Lyons' power comes more from her husband than from her socially superior position. Russell therefore suggests that gender is more important than class when it comes to power.

This answer continues on p.52. ⟶

Marking a Whole Answer

Gender roles are presented as emotionally damaging through Mrs Lyons. In Act One, Russell immediately establishes that she is childless. She then reveals that she often thinks about her imaginary child, singing "as I fold my arms around him, / He's gone." The line break before "He's gone" and the full stop after it bring the sentence to an abrupt end, emphasising Mrs Lyons' sudden return to her childless reality. Later, when talking about Edward, Mrs Lyons says "I never made him mine". This suggests that she never escapes the feeling that she has failed to fulfil the social expectation of the 1960s and 1970s that women should become mothers. Mr Lyons seems to feel less pressure to become a father, as he is against adopting a child. This implies that society puts unique pressure on women to become parents.

Mickey is used to show that gender roles can also be damaging for men. In Act Two, Mickey finds it hard to tell Linda how he feels because "the words just disappear". The image of words vanishing before they can be spoken highlights Mickey's inability to verbalise his feelings, despite knowing that Linda likes him. Here, his lack of confidence means he struggles to meet the social expectation of the late 20th century that men should pursue women. The negative impact of gender roles on men is reinforced later in the play when Mickey's desperation to provide for Linda in his role as 'husband' leads him to help with the robbery.

While gender roles are presented as powerful, Russell suggests that they are not natural. In Act One, Linda *"beams a satisfied smile"* when she excels at shooting, an activity that she would not have been expected to be good at as it was associated almost exclusively with boys and men in the late 20th century. The word *"beams"* makes it seem as though happiness is radiating from her, suggesting that she is proud of her success. This shows that she is unaware that she is not meeting gender expectations. However, in Act Two, Linda *"misses all three shots"* at the rifle-range. Her failure implies that, as a teenager, she has begun to conform to the role that she rebelled against as a child. Through this change, Russell suggests to the audience that children do not carry their immunity to gender expectations into adulthood.

Russell's presentation of gender focuses on the damaging effects of gender roles. The idea that gender is a divisive force that defines and restricts women's power runs throughout the play. Gender is presented as a more significant factor than class in limiting the lives of women, while Linda's increasing conformity to gender roles implies that they can't be avoided. Women are not alone in suffering because of their gender; Mickey's struggle shows that ideas about masculinity are also oppressive. Russell therefore ultimately shows the audience that both men and women's lives are negatively impacted by gender roles.

Grade band: .... Reasons: ....

....

....

....

....

Mark schemes — he's always got a cunning plan...

If you're really familiar with the mark scheme for your exam board, you'll know exactly what the examiner is looking for. You're being tested on several skills, so you'll need to demonstrate all of them to get top marks.

Section Five — Exam Buster

Writing Well

Spelling, punctuation and grammar (SPaG for short) might not be the most exciting things in the world, but in the exam marks will be awarded for good English, so you don't want to miss out. Using a variety of sentence structures and vocabulary will make your answer more impressive and help you to express your ideas clearly. It's a good idea to leave a few minutes at the end of the exam to check through your work for mistakes, like misspelt names. Use this page to hone your skills.

Q1 Read the sample answer below. Underline the SPaG mistakes, then correct them. One has already been done for you.

> attitude
> The Narrator changes his <u>atitude</u> towards Mrs Johnstone by the end of the play. At the
>
> start of Act one, he suggests that she is a "cruel" and stone-hearted mother, but in the final
>
> seen, he suggested that "class" might actually be to blame for the twins deaths. This implys
>
> that Mrs Johnstone is not fully responsable and shows that the Narrator's opinion has changed.

Q2 Rewrite the following sentences, using appropriate language for the exam.

a) Mrs Johnstone and Mrs Lyons are always having rows about Edward.

....

....

b) Mrs Lyons gets on Mr Lyons' nerves loads during the play.

....

....

c) Mickey, Edward and Linda are dead good friends when they're little.

....

....

d) I reckon that structure is really important for making everything tense.

....

....

Practice Questions

Now you've polished your essay-writing skills, have a bash at doing these practice questions under exam conditions. Spend five minutes doing a rough plan and about 40 minutes writing your essay. Use the techniques you've learnt in this section and leave a bit of time to check through your answer at the end.

Q1 Write about how Russell explores different attitudes to money in *Blood Brothers*.

You should write about:
- different attitudes towards money in the play
- how Russell uses these attitudes to convey important ideas.

Q2 How are Linda and the twins used to explore ideas about childhood in *Blood Brothers*?

Q3 Explore how Russell uses changes of mood in *Blood Brothers*.

You should write about:
- times when the mood of the play changes
- how Russell uses changes in mood to convey important ideas.

Q4 **"Sammy, Sammy, put that away... it's still not too late."** (Mickey, Act Two)

Write about how the characters of Mickey and Sammy are used to explore the social context of *Blood Brothers*.

Q5 **"There's a girl inside the woman / And the mother she became"** (The Narrator, Act Two)

Explain the importance of the character of Linda in *Blood Brothers*.

Answers

Section One — Analysis of Acts

Page 2: Act One
Mrs Johnstone and Mrs Lyons make an agreement

1. E.g. Russell reveals that the twins will die at the end of the play, which creates tension by making the audience wonder what will cause this.
2. a) E.g. She has no one to help her earn money or care for the children.
   b) E.g. It shows that Mrs Johnstone can't escape her problems for long.
3. The statements should be numbered 5, 1, 4, 3, 2.
4. E.g. She plays on Mrs Johnstone's fear that she may have to put some of her children into care. She says she can avoid doing this by giving a baby to her instead. / She convinces Mrs Johnstone that the baby would have a more privileged life with the Lyonses.
5. E.g. She becomes very excited and immediately puts her plan into action before Mrs Johnstone can change her mind.

Page 3: Act One
Mrs Lyons breaks the agreement

1. E.g. To emphasise that Mrs Johnstone's financial problems are relentless — she has no break from them.
2. a) False: "don't be hard on the woman"
   b) True: "The house is your domain."
   c) True: "Edward is my son. Mine."
3. Mrs Lyons, panic, job, money, Mr Lyons, baby, Edward
4. E.g. Mrs Lyons convinces her that she's committed a crime by selling her baby, so she's worried about going to prison.

Page 4: Act One
The twins become blood brothers

1. E.g. It links Mickey to violence, which makes it seem more likely that he will commit a violent crime.
2. E.g. She immediately questions Mickey to try to establish how close to the Lyonses' house he was playing, and she *grabs him* while she tells him off. / She becomes more protective over Mickey, insisting that he stays "outside the front door" to stop him from going near Edward's house.
3. E.g. The people he normally spends time with, like Sammy, don't have extra things to give away.
4. true, true, true, false, false
5. a) E.g. "Mummy, how do you spell bogey man?"
   b) E.g. "You are my son, mine"

Page 5: Act One
The children get into trouble

1. The statements should be numbered 1, 6, 3, 5, 2, 4.
2. a) She steps in to protect Mickey. E.g. "Leave him alone!"
   b) He is worried about getting into trouble. E.g. "I mean... suppose we get... caught... by a policeman."
   c) He thinks she is worrying unnecessarily. E.g. "Frightened of what, woman?"
3. E.g. She is horrified when Mr Lyons puts shoes on the table, showing that she is more paranoid than she was before.
4. E.g. He feels humiliated. This is shown through the way he takes the gun from her and ends the game so that she can't beat him any longer.

Page 6: Act One
Both families move to Skelmersdale

1. E.g. The Policeman's suggestion that Edward should be "with his own kind" causes him to change his mind about moving.
2. a) True: "Are you feeling better now, Mummy?"
   b) False: "It's not, Mickey told me."
3. E.g. She gives it to him to make sure that he has a picture of Mickey so that he'll remember him when he moves away.

4. E.g. Both Mrs Lyons and Mrs Johnstone mention seeing cows, and Sammy and Mickey ask if their house will be in the country soon after Mr Lyons says that his will be there.
5. E.g. She uses a "*posh*" voice when she tells her neighbours that she's moving, suggesting that she thinks she'll be superior to them. / She dreams about buying a car and drinking tea with the Pope, suggesting that she thinks she'll have more money and influence in Skelmersdale.

Task: Here are some key events you could have included:
- Mrs Lyons convinces Mrs Johnstone to give away a twin — this means that the twins are separated and do not know about each other's existence.
- Mickey meets Edward and they become blood brothers — this is the start of the relationship between the twins.
- The two families move to Skelmersdale — this means the twins will be living near each other again, which allows their friendship to develop.

Page 7: Act Two
Mickey and Edward get suspended from school

1. a) E.g. She can now pay the milkman on time.
   b) E.g. She prays for his wellbeing every day.
2. E.g. Similarities: Both include discussions about girls and show the boys' mothers sending them off to school lovingly. Differences: Edward goes to school in a car while Mickey takes the bus. / Edward is leaving his mother for weeks but Mickey is only leaving for the day.
3. E.g. She questions whether they are "safe", which suggests that she is worried that they haven't escaped the Johnstones. / She feels happier in Skelmersdale, saying that she's had a "very good time" with Edward during the holidays.
4. a) E.g. Both boys behave rebelliously, which shows that they have a trait in common.
   b) E.g. She is so shocked that she becomes unsteady and then she becomes desperate for an explanation from Edward.

Page 8: Act Two
The twins meet again as teenagers

1. E.g. She is pretending to like another boy to make Mickey feel jealous as she wants him to admit his feelings for her.
2. E.g. They both feel insecure about their own appearance and each one wishes that he could be like the other instead.
3. a) Mickey says "Gis a ciggie?" to Edward.
   b) Edward tells Mrs Johnstone that she's "looking very well".
   c) Edward says that Mrs Johnstone is "fabulous".
4. E.g. She lets them go to the cinema together, whereas she wouldn't let them play together in Act One. This shows that she is less worried about them being friends.
5. E.g. Mrs Johnstone manages to take control of the situation by taking the knife from Mrs Lyons. This shows that the power Mrs Lyons had over Mrs Johnstone in Act One has gone.

Page 9: Act Two
Mickey and Edward become adults

1. E.g. When Edward is cheeky to the Policeman, they join in instead of denying that he's their friend.
2. a) E.g. It suggests that they have a fun and loving friendship.
   b) E.g. The image of broken glass creates a sense of danger, suggesting that Linda and the twins' happiness will not last.
3. E.g. That he's in love with Linda.
4. E.g. He knows Mickey is struggling to reveal his feelings, so he wants to give him a chance to do so out of loyalty to him. / He knows that Linda is waiting for Mickey to ask her and he wants her to be happy.
5. a) True: "Are you mad?"
   b) False: "Some hypocrite I'd be."
   c) True: "You're great, you are, Mam."

Answers

Page 10: Act Two
The twins drift apart

1. false, true, false, false, true
2. E.g. Mickey is frustrated, because he wants to be able to support himself instead of relying on others.
3. E.g. "I always... loved you, in a way"
   E.g. It suggests that Linda and Edward may become romantically involved, which hints at how the twins will be driven further apart.
4. E.g. The Narrator refers to characters keeping their "fingers crossed", reminding the audience of Sammy and Mickey's games in Act One.
5. Mickey has an emotional breakdown in prison and develops chronic depression, which he treats with pills.
   E.g. "It seems like jail's sent him off the rails"

Page 11: Act Two
Mickey confronts Edward and the twins die

1. a) "We've gorra do somethin' about him"
   b) "I can't even see you"
   c) "Nothing cruel, / Nothing wrong"
2. E.g. She wants to drive the twins apart. / She wants to hurt Mickey.
3. E.g. Mickey questions him aggressively, asking "Does she, Eddie, does she?" in reference to whether Linda and Mickey's daughter really 'belongs' to Edward.
4. E.g. Mickey "waves" the gun instead of aiming at Edward and he screams "No", which suggests that he didn't intend to kill him.
5. E.g. Mrs Johnstone's struggle leaves the audience feeling sorry for her. This allows Russell to emphasise the message that class divides (which lead to the twins' deaths) can cause great pain. / Mrs Johnstone's inability to accept the twins' deaths means that there is no sense of closure at the end of the play. This conveys the idea that the tragic ending should not be considered acceptable, and therefore that society must change.

Task: Here are some points you could have included:
- Seven: E.g. Their friendship is formed quickly and effortlessly. They admire one another's differences, but Mickey seems the more powerful of the two.
- Fourteen: E.g. Their friendship seems even closer — Mickey confides in Edward about how difficult he finds it to tell Linda how he feels about her, and Edward tries to support him.
- Eighteen: E.g. Their relationship is strained after Mickey's redundancy as he is forced to grow up before Edward. Their differences seem more significant to Mickey than they used to.
- Twenties: E.g. They are no longer friends and Mickey resents the fact that Edward has provided him with a job and a house. Edward now has more power than Mickey.

Page 12: Skills Focus — Using Quotes

1. accurate, relevant, irrelevant, embedded, important, repeat
   (Other answers are also possible.)
2. Good quote usage: b) and c) *[relevant and well embedded]*
   Bad quote usage: a) *[irrelevant]*, d) *[repeats point above too closely]* and e) *[too long, not embedded]*
3. You could have rewritten the examples as follows:
   a) Mickey has a good relationship with Mrs Johnstone. He tells her she's "great" and confides in her about Linda's pregnancy.
   d) Mrs Johnstone thinks that she'll be able to "begin again" in Skelmersdale.
   e) In Act Two, Mickey feels that he and Edward are not as close because he "grew up" while Edward "didn't need to".

Page 13: Skills Focus — P.E.E.D.

1. a) The Explain stage is missing. A sentence should be added to explain the quote, for example:
   This language associated with dark magic suggests that Mrs Lyons' increasing paranoia means she is no longer thinking rationally.

b) The Example stage is missing. A specific example or a quote should be added to back up the initial statement, for example: In Act Two, the Narrator taunts Mrs Lyons with rhetorical questions, asking if she feels "Free from the broken looking glass" after Edward shows her his locket.
c) The Develop stage is missing. The answer should be extended by explaining the effect on the audience or linking the example to another aspect of the play, for example:
The suddenness of this transition between the songs accelerates the pace of the play, which further heightens the sense of excitement.

Section Two — Characters

Page 14: Mrs Johnstone

1. a) E.g. She hopes that her new job will solve her money issues.
   b) E.g. She orders things from catalogues that she can't afford.
2. E.g. It stops her from having a close relationship with Edward as she believes Mrs Lyons' invented superstition that the twins will both die if they learn that they are brothers.
3. a) E.g. She has become a stronger character since Act One.
   b) E.g. She is protective of her children.
4. E.g. No, because she hugs Mickey and Edward, which shows that she's warm-hearted. She also tries hard to support Mickey through his depression. **Or** e.g. Yes, because she agrees to give away her child and tries to distance herself from Edward.

Task: You should have written your entry from Mrs Johnstone's point of view. Here are some points you could have included:
- Mrs Johnstone decides to give away one of the twins because she can't afford to keep them both. Some of her children are already at risk of being taken into care.
- She believes that Mrs Lyons will give her child a better life because the Lyonses can afford to buy things like "A bike with *both* wheels on".
- Mrs Johnstone is reluctant to swear on the Bible, which suggests that she's uneasy about making the deal.
- She feels "*afraid*" after Mrs Lyons leaves, which suggests that she isn't happy with the idea of giving away a child.

Page 15: Mr and Mrs Lyons

1. false, true, true, true
2. E.g. She is judgemental when she calls Mickey and Sammy "boys like that". The way she hits Edward makes her seem harsh and impulsive to the audience.
3. E.g. "They're... drawing him away from me."
   E.g. She becomes possessive over him and tries to control him by limiting his freedom.
4. a) E.g. "You've been a perfect poppet"
   b) E.g. "Mummy will read the story, Edward."

Task: Here are some points you could have included:
- Stage directions used to present increasing superstition.
  - Laughs at Mrs Johnstone's fear of shoes on table, but "*sweeps*" shoes off table later on in the play.
  - Verb "*sweeps*" = describes sudden movement, mirrors Mrs Johnstone's reaction. Shows attitude change.
  - Increasing superstition makes Mrs Lyons seems more fearful = shows that she is losing control.
- Driven mad by paranoia over Edward and the Johnstones.
  - Repetition of "mad woman" by "*chanting*" kids.
  - Offstage chanting = sounds like voices in Mrs Lyons' head. This staging reinforces impression of madness.
  - Her madness emphasises that pact has consequences for all involved = eventually destroys her mental stability.
- Loses authority over Mrs Johnstone
  - Act One — uses imperatives and short commands when firing Mrs Johnstone. Act Two — questions and conditional sentences when she fails to bribe Mrs Johnstone.
  - Contrast = commanding tone in Act One, negotiating in Act Two. Highlights loss of authority.

Answers

- Mrs Lyons has lost power that middle class had over working class in late 20th century — she can't impose this authority, makes her seem weaker.

Page 16: Mickey Johnstone

1. a) E.g. *"suspiciously taking one"*
   b) E.g. *"almost in tears"*
2. E.g. He struggles to tell Linda how he feels about her. / He wishes he could be more like Edward. / He's insecure about his acne.
3. a) E.g. He becomes angry easily. He is pessimistic about his situation.
   b) E.g. He dismisses him and feels as if he has less in common with him. He resents Edward for having the freedom of no responsibilities.
4. E.g. Mickey's speech is stilted when he says "D' y' know who told me about... you... an' Linda..." This suggests that his thoughts are scattered as he is overwhelmed by anger.
Task: You should have written your answers from Edward's point of view. Here are some points you could have included:
   • Accepting — Mickey doesn't care when Sammy points out that Edward is from a different class.
   • Forthcoming — he happily reveals lots of things about his life to Edward and shares his knowledge with him.
   • Friendly — he offers to be Edward's blood brother even though they have only just met.
   • Mischievous — he enjoys teaching Edward swear words.

Page 17: Edward Lyons

1. E.g. "Hi-ya, Mickey." / "She's off her beam, my ma". Any valid explanation, e.g. He is easily influenced by Mickey, who also uses informal language. / He can communicate easily with people who have a different background to him.
2. a) E.g. "Take as many as you want."
   b) E.g. "Hello, Mrs Johnstone. How are you?"
   c) E.g. "Why... why is a job so important?"
3. E.g. He finds it hard to speak to girls as a teenager, partly because he rarely has contact with them. When he tries to dance with Linda's friend, she tells him to "gettoff".
4. E.g. Agree, because he encourages Mickey to ask Linda out despite being in love with her and he gets Mickey a job even though their relationship has broken down. **Or** e.g. Disagree, because he proposes to Linda when she is with Mickey and betrays Mickey by having an affair with her.
Exam Practice:
   Your answer should have an introduction, several paragraphs developing different ideas and a conclusion.
   You may have covered some of the following points:
   • Russell uses Edward to show how a person's upbringing influences their identity. In Act One, Edward addresses Mrs Lyons as "mummy", which makes his class identity seem stronger as it is a word more commonly used by middle-class children. This shows how his upbringing has influenced his identity. Almost immediately after meeting Mickey, Edward begins to use informal language, highlighting Mickey's influence on his identity.
   • Russell uses staging to present Edward as insecure about his identity. During 'That Guy', Edward expresses self-consciousness about his appearance while Mickey sings about his positive perception of Edward at the same time. This contrast emphasises both boys' insecurity. This song has the same melody as the song 'My Child' from Act One, which reminds the audience of the fact that Edward's identity as a Lyons and a member of the middle class is also insecure.
   • Russell uses Edward to suggest that children are less aware of class identity than adults. In Act One, Russell contrasts Mrs Lyons' disapproval of Mickey with Edward's insistence that Mickey is his "best friend". This highlights Edward's innocence about the divides that often kept children of different classes apart in the late 20th century. Russell uses

Edward's friendship with Mickey to suggest to the audience that children are not naturally prejudiced about class, but rather that society teaches them to be prejudiced about those with different class identities.

Page 18: Linda

1. a) E.g. "I'm not scared, either."
   b) E.g. "look on the bright side of it"
   c) E.g. "I just love you. I love you!"
2. Act One: e.g. She finds the idea of being cheeky to policemen funny.
   Act Two: e.g. She jokes with Edward before he goes to university.
3. E.g. She is described as the "girl in the middle of the pair", which suggests that she is becoming an object of both twins' desire. She misses the target at the rifle range, which implies that she is losing the power she had in Act One.
4. E.g. She feels trapped by her responsibilities and her affair with Edward makes her feel playful and free again. / Edward shows he cares about her by trying to find a house for her and Mickey.
Task: Here are some points you could have included:
   • E.g. In the bus scene in Act Two, Linda stands up for Mickey when Sammy tries to make him follow him off the bus. This shows that Linda continues to try to protect Mickey from Sammy as they grow up.
   • Before the robbery, Linda suspects that Sammy has persuaded Mickey to break the law and tries to stop Mickey from doing it. This shows that, just as in Act One, she tries to keep Mickey out of trouble.

Page 19: Sammy Johnstone

1. E.g. Mickey admires Sammy for spitting and playing with matches. This suggests that Sammy's bad behaviour may be setting a poor example for Mickey.
2. a) E.g. "He's a friggin' poshy."
   b) E.g. *"He goes into a fantasy shoot-out."*
   c) E.g. "Come on, gang, let's go."
3. E.g. Sammy seems less like a victim to the audience because he chooses crime, rather than being forced into it by desperation like Mickey. This makes it harder to forgive Sammy for his actions.
4. E.g. He refers to guns as "shooters", which makes him seem immature. / He says "Y' don't get up again" after being shot, which echoes his rhyme "I got y' / I shot y'" from Act One.
Task: Here are some events you could have included:
   • As a child, he steals Mickey's toys and Linda accuses him of stealing money and cigarettes from her house.
   • The Policeman implies that the nine-year-old Sammy has already been in trouble with the police.
   • He goes to court after burning down his school.
   • He attacks a bus conductor with a knife.
   • He commits robbery and shoots the garage attendant.

Page 20: The Narrator

1. E.g. The fact that he has no fixed character makes him seem untrustworthy — the audience doesn't know who he really is, or why he is able to take on these different roles. / It suggests that he's an unsympathetic character as he often behaves in a cold-hearted and judgemental way in these roles.
2. E.g. His use of imagery related to bad omens, such as "the salt's been spilled", makes it seem as if he is threatening Mrs Johnstone with his knowledge of her future.
3. E.g. He appears as the bus conductor when Mrs Johnstone is waving off Sammy and Mickey.
   Any valid explanation, e.g. His arrival suggests that Mrs Johnstone's happiness won't last, which dampens the scene's light-hearted mood.

Answers

4. E.g. The Narrator often comes on stage and then doesn't speak or sing for a while. For example, he "*watches*" Linda phone Edward in Act Two. His silence at a time when things seem to be going wrong makes him seem sinister.

Page 21: Skills Focus — Making Links

1. You could have used the following examples:
    Mrs Johnstone — She plans to go back to work soon after giving birth to the twins so that her family can "live like kings". / She refuses to move away from Skelmersdale when Mrs Lyons tries to bribe her.
    Mickey — He goes to Edward's house even though Mrs Johnstone has forbidden him from doing so. / He responds sarcastically when his teacher tries to convince him that his education is important.
    Edward — He refuses to tell Mrs Lyons why he wears the locket, claiming that it is "just a secret". / He hides his feelings for Linda for several years.

2. You could have made the following points:
    Linda — She shows loyalty to Mickey for most of the play, e.g. She protects Mickey from Sammy and the other children when they bully him. / She tells Sammy "He's stayin' here" when he tries to make Mickey get off the bus.
    Mrs Lyons — She becomes aggressive when she feels threatened, e.g. She hits Edward when he calls her a "fuckoff". / She attacks Mrs Johnstone with a knife when Mrs Johnstone refuses to leave Skelmersdale.
    Sammy — He is uncaring, e.g. He doesn't protect Mickey from the other children in Act One. / He leaves Mickey behind when trying to get away from the police after the petrol station robbery.

Page 22: Practice Questions

Your answers should have an introduction, several paragraphs developing different ideas and a conclusion.
You may have covered some of the following points:

1. • Russell shows that Mrs Johnstone and Edward's relationship has been damaged by their separation. In Act Two, Edward addresses her as "Mrs Johnstone", in a scene where Mickey repeatedly calls her "Mam". By showing Mickey's familiarity and Edward's polite respect on stage at the same time, Russell highlights the distance in Edward and Mrs Johnstone's relationship. The way that Mrs Johnstone treats the twins as a "pair" in this scene suggests that she sees Edward as her son, making their lack of closeness seem tragic to the audience.
    • Mrs Johnstone's behaviour towards Edward highlights her strong maternal instincts. In Act One, she "*Cradles him*" when he is upset. The verb "*Cradles*", which usually applies to babies rather than seven-year-olds, suggests that Mrs Johnstone is trying to go back in time and fulfil the protective, nurturing role denied to her by Mrs Lyons. This behaviour contrasts with her attempts to push Edward away earlier in the act, which implies that her maternal instincts are stronger than her fear of Mrs Lyons' invented superstition.
    • Edward's attitude towards Mrs Johnstone highlights his lack of class prejudice. Mrs Lyons encourages him to see himself as superior to the Johnstones, but Edward admires Mrs Johnstone, calling her "smashing" and "fabulous". These positive adjectives show that he hasn't been influenced by Mrs Lyons' snobbery. His lack of prejudice may have seemed unusual to an audience in the 1980s, when society was strongly divided by class.

2. • Russell presents the Narrator as mysterious through his use of staging. At the end of the play, the lighting dims to reveal that the Narrator has been "*watching*" the twins' death scene. This shows that the Narrator has been present on stage but has gone unnoticed, which makes him seem like a ghostly figure. The contrast between the Narrator's passiveness here and the way he drives the action elsewhere in the play makes him seem even more mysterious.

• Russell presents the Narrator as classless to make him seem mysterious. In some scenes, he uses omission, for example saying "y'" instead of "you", mimicking speech that would have been heard on working-class estates in the late 20th century. However, at other times, he uses Standard English, such as "He always knows where to find you". This contrast implies that the Narrator doesn't belong to any social class, making his identity unclear. The play's other main characters do have clear class identities, so the Narrator's classlessness makes him stand out, heightening the mystery about his background.
• The Narrator takes on multiple roles, which creates uncertainty about his identity. When he becomes the Gynaecologist, Mrs Johnstone recognises him as the Milkman from an earlier scene. Russell uses this recognition to show that the Narrator, not the actor who plays him, is taking on the various roles, making his true identity seem like a mystery. In the rest of the play, the Narrator is often only visible to the audience, but he becomes visible to other characters when playing these additional roles. This suggests that he can control when he is seen, which adds to his mysterious nature.

3. • Mickey is presented as suddenly powerless after his loss of employment in Act Two. Mickey uses the verb "disappeared" to describe his job loss to Edward. The word "disappeared" implies that something has vanished suddenly, and is often related to magic, which suggests that Mickey's job has vanished due to forces beyond his control. Russell uses Mickey's powerlessness to reflect the impact that job losses had on working class people during the economic downturn of the 1970s and 1980s.
    • Mickey's descent into poverty makes him more willing to commit crime. In Act Two, he tries to stop Sammy robbing the bus conductor. However, later in the play Russell structures the scene in which Sammy convinces Mickey to help rob the petrol station so that Mickey only agrees to help Sammy after confirming that he'll be paid. This suggests that he is motivated mainly by his need for money. His situation reflects that of the men who turned to crime during the economic downturn of the 1970s and 1980s due to unemployment and poverty.
    • Mickey's unemployment is linked to the breakdown of his relationship with Edward. Russell structures the play so that the twins have their first real argument just after the song where Mickey is made redundant. The fact that these events happen so close together suggests that Mickey's redundancy contributes to the breakdown of the twins' relationship. The twins don't appear together on stage again until their confrontation in the final scene, reinforcing the idea that their relationship never recovers after Mickey's redundancy.

4. • Russell uses Mrs Lyons to drive the plot forwards. The Narrator describes Mrs Lyons' idea to take one of the twins as something that "can / Take root and grow", before saying that it "Grew as surely as a seed". The shift from the present tense "can / Take root" to the past tense verb "Grew" shows how Mrs Lyons' plan goes from having potential to being put into action almost immediately. This accelerates the pace of the play, and gives the impression that an unstoppable chain of events has been set in motion. Later in the scene, the pact is "born" not long after it was "conceived", reinforcing the idea that Mrs Lyons' idea propels the plot forward.
    • Russell uses Mrs Lyons' attitude towards Mickey to explore ideas about class prejudice. After Edward swears at her in Act One, Mrs Lyons says he has learned "filth" from Mickey. The word "filth" suggests that Mrs Lyons sees Mickey as something unclean that will contaminate her child. This reflects the negative views that many middle-class people held about working-class people in the late 20th century. Russell uses this scene to show the audience that adults teach class prejudice to children, as Mrs Lyons seeks to pass her negative views on to her son.

Answers

- The character of Mrs Lyons helps Russell to convey a moral message to the audience. In Act Two, the Narrator says that the devil "always knows where to find" her. This indicates that Mrs Lyons will be punished for her treatment of Mrs Johnstone, which encourages the audience to think about how they treat others. In this way, Russell gives the play elements of a cautionary tale, a form in which the listener or reader is warned about the dangers of behaving immorally.

5. • Russell presents Mrs Johnstone as a victim of poverty. In Act One, Mrs Johnstone *stands alone* while her children repeat "I'm starvin'" off stage. This offstage chorus of voices creates the impression that she is surrounded by demands that she can't meet, which highlights the financial struggle that many single, working-class mothers faced in the late 20th century. In Act Two, Mrs Johnstone is less of a victim of poverty, as her finances are stable enough for her to not be tempted by the "thousands" that Mrs Lyons offers her to move.

- Mrs Johnstone is presented as a victim of fate. In Act Two, the Narrator's repeated line "the devil's got your number" changes to suggest that the devil is getting closer each time. The the last time this line appears, the Narrator says that the devil will call Mrs Johnstone "TODAY!" This makes Mrs Johnstone seem like a victim by making it seem as if she is being pursued by fate. The fact that the audience has already seen Mrs Johnstone's fate unfold in the narrator's first speech strengthens the idea that she can't escape it.

- Mrs Johnstone is a victim of manipulation. In Act One, Mrs Lyons takes advantage of Mrs Johnstone by claiming that there is a superstition about parted twins that she is unaware of, after which Mrs Johnstone immediately asks "What? What?" The repetition of "What?" makes it seem as though Mrs Johnstone is frantically hanging on Mrs Lyons' every word, which leaves her vulnerable to Mrs Lyons' lies. This manipulation affects her until the end of the play, as she only reveals the twins' true relationship when they are about to die.

Section Three — Context and Themes

Page 23: Liverpool in the Late Twentieth Century

1. set, industries, economy, working, support
   (Other answers are also possible.)
2. E.g. Mickey struggles financially after being made redundant. This leads Mickey to accept Sammy's offer of money in exchange for helping with the robbery.
3. E.g. It had rich areas and poor areas that were situated very close to one another.
4. a) E.g. Mrs Johnstone is told in a letter that she is being moved to Skelmersdale.
   b) E.g. She has a very idealistic view of Skelmersdale, which she believes has "pure" air and huge gardens. / Mrs Johnstone believes that the family will be able to "begin again" in Skelmersdale.

Pages 24-25: Money and Social Class

1. E.g. He is able to go to university. / He gets a well-respected job.
2. true, true, false, true
3. E.g. She can offer Edward a privileged lifestyle than Mrs Johnstone.
   Any valid explanation, e.g. She makes Mrs Johnstone feel as though she'd be doing the right thing for her child by giving him away.
4. E.g. Many of them are probably working-class, so they're under pressure to start earning money. Further education probably isn't an option, making school seem unimportant.
5. E.g. It shows he holds class prejudices. Both boys are caught doing the same thing, but he treats them differently. He describes Mickey's actions as "serious", but Edward's as "a prank".

6. E.g. Mickey can't rely on his family to support him financially, so he has to get a job and be responsible at an earlier age than Edward.
7. E.g. His willingness to work in terrible conditions suggests that he's desperate. The image of him crawling creates pity because it implies that unemployment has taken his dignity.
8. a) E.g. "why is a job so important?"
   b) E.g. "look, next week I'll pay y'—"
   c) E.g. "think where y' could take Linda if you had cash like that"
9. a) E.g. He tries to give Mickey money when Mickey is unemployed.
   b) E.g. No, because she assumes that Mrs Johnstone won't be able to refuse such a large sum of money. Mrs Lyons expects Mrs Johnstone to value money because she is poor. **Or** e.g. Yes, because she doesn't seem shocked by Mrs Johnstone's refusal. She quickly gives up on trying to bribe her, suggesting that she didn't expect it to work.

Pages 26-27: Fate and Superstition

1. E.g. To make events seem more tragic. As the audience watches their friendship develop, they already know both twins will die.
2. E.g. When Mickey is searching for Edward at the end of the play and Mrs Johnstone is trying to catch him. Any valid explanation, e.g. It creates tension as it suggests that Mickey and Mrs Johnstone are both being pursued by the devil.
3. E.g. Fate keeps bringing Mickey and Edward back together. Even though Mrs Lyons moved Edward away, the two families have ended up living near each other again.
4. Narrator, audience, twins, remind, deaths, inevitable
   (Other answers are also possible.)
5. E.g. It suggests that, although her belief in fate gets stronger, she still thinks she can influence it through her own actions.
6. E.g. It makes the audience feel tense, as these superstitions emphasise the idea that Mickey and Edward are doomed.
7. E.g. Her fear of the superstition is so strong that she doesn't dare take Edward back or reveal the truth. She only tells the truth when she feels the twins' lives are already in danger.
8. E.g. The way she *rushes* to the table suggests that the sight of the shoes has panicked her. The scene suddenly *snaps* to the children, emphasising her fear that Edward is at risk.
9. b) Argument for, e.g. If Mrs Johnstone hadn't kept Edward's identity a secret because of her fear of superstition, Mickey might not have reacted so badly when he found out.
   Argument against, e.g. Even though the twins die, the audience knows that Mrs Lyons just invented the superstition about their deaths.
   c) Argument for, e.g. The play's cyclical structure suggests that Mickey and Edward are unable to escape their fate.
   Argument against, e.g. Lots of small decisions led to the twins' deaths. Characters could have made different decisions.
Task: Here are some points you might have included:
   - Fate is an important source of tension in the play.
     - Start of play, audience shown a *re-enactment of the final moments of the play* (Mickey and Edward's deaths).
     - Dramatic irony creates tension, wonder how / why the twins will die.
     - This tension sustained by Narrator. Constant reminder: "the devil's got your number". Word "number" makes it seem like they've been specifically picked out, deaths are inevitable.
   - Fate helps Russell explore ideas about working-class life.
     - Linda and Mrs Johnstone share very similar fate (mothers, bearing a lot of responsibility, cleaning)
     - Suggests working-class women are destined to share the same fate. Class system decides their destinies.
     - Echoed in the way Mickey ends up mirroring Sammy, even though they have different personalities.
   - Exploration of role of fate is linked to Russell's message about social responsibility.
     - Russell doesn't give clear indication of whether fate is

Answers

actually to blame.

   - Makes audience question role of other factors (superstition / social class).

   - Huge rise in social inequality during 1970s and 1980s. Audience at time may therefore have been particularly receptive to exploring role of class vs. role of fate.

Page 28: Childhood and Growing Up

1. E.g. Mickey has a closer relationship with his mum than Edward. / Mickey comes from a large family where he has to compete for attention, but Edward gets lots of attention from his parents.

2. E.g. The twins' violent deaths seem more tragic, as the audience can remember the twins as innocent children.

3. E.g. The children's games in Act One include references to American popular culture, like bazookas and Al Capone.

4. a) E.g. "in term time we hardly ever see a girl"
   b) E.g. "the words just disappear"

5. E.g. Mickey seems more mature than Edward, who can't understand why Mickey needs a job so badly. Mickey sees Edward as a "kid" because he can't understand the pressure Mickey is under.

Page 29: Friendship

1. a) E.g. Mickey comes up with the idea of becoming blood brothers and makes Edward swear an oath.
   b) E.g. Edward has much more power than Mickey — he helps Linda to find Mickey a new house and a job.

2. E.g. He doesn't spend much time with other children, so his close friendship with Linda and Mickey gives him a chance to be part of their games and adventures and break free from his strict upbringing.

3. E.g. "you make me sick" (Mickey)

4. E.g. The twins' adult friendship is complicated by their romantic feelings for Linda. Both twins are attracted to her, and this is ultimately what causes the most conflict between them.

Task: Here are some points you might have included:
- Mrs Johnstone — She helps Edward to remember Mickey by giving him the locket. / She lets the boys spend time together. / She plays a part in their deaths. When she says that Edward is Mickey's twin, Mickey becomes "*almost uncontrollable with rage*" and fires the gun.
- Mrs Lyons — She separates the boys by moving to Skelmersdale. / She points out Edward and Linda's affair to Mickey, causing conflict between the twins.
- Linda — She has adventures with the twins when they're younger, which makes their friendship stronger. / She's linked to the twins' deaths, as her affair with Edward makes Mickey confront him.

Page 30: Identity

1. E.g. Any big differences between them have probably been caused by their upbringing, as they're genetically alike.

2. true, true, false, false

3. E.g. He is generous about sharing his possessions. When Mickey wants a sweet, he says "Take as many as you want."

4. E.g. To highlight the fact that the songs focus on the same subject, as they both explore attitudes towards identity.

5. E.g. Yes, because the play suggests that a person's opportunities have a big impact on their identity. If Mickey had been given to Mrs Lyons, he probably wouldn't have left school so early or have been made redundant. **Or** e.g. No, because even though Sammy and Mickey have the same upbringing, they are very different people. This suggests that if Mickey had received the same upbringing as Edward, he wouldn't necessarily have been exactly like Edward.

Exam Practice:
Your answer should have an introduction, several paragraphs developing different ideas and a conclusion.

You may have covered some of the following points:
- Identity is an important source of tension in the play. Russell structures the play so that the audience is aware of Mickey and Edward's true identities long before the twins learn the truth. This dramatic irony creates suspense throughout the play, as the audience wonders if they'll discover the truth before they both die. The tension is heightened by the way fate keeps reuniting the twins, as it suggests that their real identities can't be suppressed.
- The theme of identity is used to present ideas about social class. In the final scene, Mickey screams that he "could have been" Edward. This suggests that he believes the differences between him and Edward are a result of the advantages that Edward's middle-class upbringing has given him, which reflects the better opportunities that middle-class people often had in the late 20th century. This shows that class is a divisive force in the twins' lives. Mickey's attitude reinforces the idea that nurture can have a stronger influence on a person's life than nature.
- Russell shows that a person's natural identity has an important influence on their personality and behaviour. In the song 'That Guy', they finish each other's rhymes in alternate sets of lines. These shared rhymes and interlocking lines make it seem as though they are unconsciously composing the same song. This suggests that there is a natural link between them that influences them both. Furthermore, the twins' use of an unpredictable, almost cheeky, half-rhyme ("attacked me" with "acne") at the same time suggests that they also share a sense of humour and a disregard for established conventions at this point in the play.

Page 31: Gender

1. fixed, house, work, family, Mickey, Linda
   (Other answers are also possible.)

2. E.g. Traditionally, women were just expected to look after the house and the children, but Mrs Johnstone also works.

3. E.g. In the 1960s and 1970s, a woman's role was focused on the family and home. As a result, Mrs Lyons' inability to have children might make her feel like a failure as a woman.

4. E.g. He might be suggesting that working-class women are destined to endure the same hardships as Mrs Johnstone.

5. E.g. Yes, because a 1980s audience would have expected a good father to provide for his family by working. **Or** e.g. No, because they would have expected him to be there for Edward as a father, and he is absent too often to do this.

Task: Here are some points you might have included:
- Mr Johnstone would have provided his family with an income. The family's financial situation would probably have been more stable, so Mrs Johnstone might not have needed to work.
- It's likely that Mrs Johnstone would have kept both twins. This might have prevented the deterioration in Mickey and Edward's relationship, as the tensions that arise between them as adults are mainly due to class differences.
- Edward probably wouldn't have gone to university, or grown up to have a job as a councillor. He would have been working-class and therefore would have left school at the same time as Mickey to find a job.

Page 32: Skills Focus — Writing about Context

1. a) the widespread unemployment caused by the decline of traditional industries in the 1970s and 1980s affected the working class particularly badly. / one of the most common British surnames.
   b) the fixed role that many women in Britain had in the second half of the 20th century. / In the 1960s and 1970s, many people believed that a woman's role was to have children and look after the household. / this view was very firmly rooted in British society at the time.

2. E.g. Between the 1960s and the 1980s, working-class pupils

often had to find a job to support their families once they left school. Middle-class students like Edward usually didn't take on this responsibility so soon, as they had more opportunity to go to university.

Page 33: Practice Questions

Your answers should have an introduction, several paragraphs developing different ideas and a conclusion.
You may have covered some of the following points:

1. • The twins' acceptance of each other shows the simplicity of childhood friendship. In the song 'My Friend', Edward admires Mickey for swearing "like a soldier" just after Mickey wishes he could "talk properly like" Edward. Expletives are generally associated with working-class characters in the play, while middle-class characters speak formally. Therefore, the twins' admiration of each other's characteristics shows the simplicity of their friendship, as it implies that they are unaware of the class differences that these features represent. Russell uses this innocent friendship to suggest to the audience that the class divide that existed in society at the time the play is set was not natural but taught.
   • Mickey and Edward's relationship shows that friendship becomes complicated in adulthood. Towards the end of the play, Mickey says to Edward "you still are a kid, aren't ye?" The word "kid" gives Mickey's speech a condescending tone and the rhetorical question makes his observation sound taunting. His attitude suggests that having so much adult responsibility when Edward has so little has become a source of tension in their friendship. Their increasingly difficult relationship is foreshadowed by the Narrator earlier in the play, when he regrets that Linda and the twins can't be teenagers "for ever".
   • The serious attitude that both Mickey and Edward have towards their relationship as children implies that friendship is meaningful. Russell uses staging to highlight the formal way the pair commit to their friendship when they make their oaths and "clamp hands". The image of clasped hands makes them seem unified to the audience, while sealing the pact with blood symbolises their unbreakable bond. These solemn acts show how important their friendship is to them. When Edward moves away, the twins silently "clasp hands", which implies that they still value the promises they made.

2. • The theme of childhood is used to develop ideas about class. As a child, Mickey defends Edward when he is called a "poshy". However, Mickey later speaks scathingly of "Councillor Eddie Lyons". Through the use of Edward's title, Mickey bitterly acknowledges the additional power that Edward's privileged upbringing has given him, and hints that this is the source of their conflict. The contrast between the twins' childhood friendship and their strained adult relationship therefore suggests that class division is damaging. This message would have been especially relevant in the 1980s, as class divides were deepening due to the recession.
   • Russell uses the theme of childhood to create sympathy for women in the play. In Act Two, the Narrator notes that "There's a girl inside the woman" when describing Linda. This image suggests that Linda's childhood has ended too early, as her 'girlish' nature is still present but has to be suppressed due to her responsibilities as a wife and mother. The idea that youth ends early for women is also shown in the opening scene, when the stage directions indicate that the thirty-year-old Mrs Johnstone looks "fifty", implying that she has aged prematurely.
   • Childhood innocence is an important source of comedy in the play. In Act One, when Mickey describes the plate Sammy has in his head, he tells Edward that it's like one "you have bread off". The way that this silly image is presented so sincerely by Mickey makes the audience laugh at his childish view of the world. Russell uses the comedy in the children's scenes to make Act One feel light-hearted and create a contrast with the more menacing tone of Act Two, which

adds to the impression that the twins move closer to their doom as they grow up.

3. • Russell structures the scene where Mrs Lyons puts the shoes on the table to emphasise the power of superstition. Immediately after Mrs Johnstone sees the shoes, she asks Mrs Lyons "what are y' trying to do?" before telling her to "take them off". This blunt question and direct command make Mrs Johnstone sound confrontational, in contrast to the respectful attitude she shows earlier in the scene. Her sudden change in attitude highlights the power that superstition has over her. Mrs Johnstone puts her job at risk in this scene by making demands on her employer, which further emphasises the power of superstition.
   • Russell uses the Narrator to question the role of superstition in the play. In the Narrator's last speech, he asks whether superstition or class is to blame for the twins' deaths. This question encourages the audience to reflect on what causes the tragic ending, which suggests that superstition is not solely to blame. This helps Russell to achieve his aim of encouraging the audience to consider the impact of class on people's lives.
   • The superstition surrounding the twins is presented as dangerous through the way an invented superstition becomes reality. At the end of the play, Mickey shoots Edward when he loses control after realising that he "could have been him!" This suggests that Mrs Lyons' prophecy does come true; learning their true identity is what triggers the twins' tragic deaths. The violent verbs used to describe how Mickey's gun "explodes and blows Edward apart" and the police guns "explode, blowing Mickey away", further emphasise the destructive nature of superstition.

4. • In the play, Russell uses sequential scenes to present working-class life as limiting. In Act Two, a scene showing Edward at school, where there's "Talk of Oxbridge", is followed by Mickey telling his teacher that school won't help him get a job. These consecutive scenes emphasise that Edward is likely to go on to an elite university while Mickey must think about earning money, which shows that his future is predetermined by his working-class life. These scenes suggest that middle-class life also involves a kind of limitation, as Edward's future at university is apparently set out when he is only fourteen.
   • Russell uses Edward to present misconceptions about the role of welfare payments in working-class life. In Act Two, Edward says he'd "draw the dole" and "live like a bohemian" if he was unemployed. The word "bohemian" suggests that he sees living on welfare payments as a life of freedom, which reflects his naive view that taking these payments was a choice, rather than a necessity. Later in the play, Mickey's descent into crime and his depression confirm how misinformed Edward is in this scene.
   • Russell uses the Johnstones to present hardship as a key part of working-class life. Their experiences reflect stereotypes about how working-class people lived in the 1960s; the Johnstones have to pay for things in instalments, suffer from unstable employment and live in overcrowded conditions. By making the Johnstones easily identifiable as a working-class family to a 1980s audience, Russell presents the hardships they face as representative of working-class life in general in that period. This presentation of working-class life as difficult encourages the audience to feel sympathy for the Johnstones.

5. • Russell presents Mrs Johnstone as a motherly figure by showing that she is an experienced parent. Early in Act One, Mrs Johnstone says that having children is "like clockwork" for her. The term "clockwork" suggests that childbirth is an automatic and effortless process for her and that pregnancy is a familiar routine. This emphasises her vast experience of having children, establishing her as a motherly figure early in the play. Mrs Johnstone's experience as a mother of a large family reflects that of many working-class women in the

Answers

1960s, when access to contraception was often limited.

- Mrs Lyons is presented as a motherly figure through her supportive attitude towards her children. When she learns that the twins are going to see a pornographic film, she tells them "Go on, y' randy little sods." This encouragement suggests that she understands and supports their need to explore their sexuality. Her role as a supportive mother is reinforced later in the act when she agrees almost immediately and without question to support Mickey and Linda through Linda's pregnancy.

- Russell presents Mrs Johnstone as a flawed motherly figure by suggesting that, at times, she is an irresponsible parent. When Sammy burns his school down, she claims that it is "easily done" if teachers let pupils use chemicals. Her unconcerned reaction and willingness to blame the teacher suggests that her love for her children sometimes blinds her to reality. This approach echoes the way she agrees to look in the catalogue for the things her children ask for, despite not being able to afford them.

Section Four — The Writer's Techniques

Page 34: Structure in 'Blood Brothers'

1.   E.g. To make the twins' deaths seem unavoidable.
2.   E.g. The twins are born immediately after Mrs Johnstone and Mrs Lyons make their pact.
     Any valid explanation, e.g. It makes it seem as though Mrs Johnstone can't escape from the agreement.
3. a) E.g. It accelerates the pace by showing several years passing quickly.
   b) E.g. So he can show that their teenage years are happy and carefree while highlighting how fleeting these years are.
4.   E.g. The audience knows that the twins really are brothers but the twins don't. Their ignorance creates tension.
5.   E.g. To show that their relationships with their children differ. Mrs Johnstone fears for both twins' lives, whereas Mrs Lyons fears losing power over Edward.

Exam Practice:
   Your answer should have an introduction, several paragraphs developing different ideas and a conclusion.
   You may have covered some of the following points:

- The play's structure is used to explore the theme of fate. The play begins with a "*re-enactment*" of the final scene, in which the twins die. The cyclical structure this creates suggests that the twins' tragic fate is unavoidable. The idea that fate is a powerful force is emphasised through the way that the twins keep meeting one another despite their mothers' attempts to keep them apart.

- Russell uses recurring melodies to create links between different scenes. In the song 'That Guy' in Act Two, the twins sing about wanting to be more like each other. This song repeats the melody of the Act One song 'My Child', in which Mrs Johnstone and Mrs Lyons sing about giving one of the twins a middle-class life. By linking these scenes together with this melody, Russell highlights the conflict between Edward's 'true' identity and his middle-class upbringing. This link reinforces the idea that Edward is drawn to the Johnstones, making Mrs Lyons' fear of losing him seem more realistic to the audience.

- Sequential scenes show the contrast between the twins' schools. In Act Two, Edward's teacher uses formal sentence structures like "Am I to punish you, Lyons?" In the next scene, Mickey's teacher calls Perkins a "borin' little turd". The word "turd" likens the pupil to foul waste and suggests that the teacher considers him worthless. The juxtaposition between this dismissive attitude and Edward's teacher's formal tone emphasises how different the twins' schools are. This stark contrast reflects the fact that there was a strong class divide in education in the late 20th century.

Page 35: Form in 'Blood Brothers'

1.   E.g. The Narrator reveals the end of the play in the prologue and comments on events that contribute to the tragic ending of the play, such as the mothers' pact in Act One.
2.   E.g. It might imply that the twins are to blame for their fate, which would weaken Russell's message that their deaths are caused by class divisions.
3.   E.g. It gives the audience an insight into the twins' insecurities, which creates sympathy for them.
4. a) E.g. The Narrator encourages the audience to consider what part social class plays in the twins' deaths.
   b) E.g. The Narrator tells parts of the story in rhyming couplets.
Task: Here are some points you could have included:
- 'My Friend' reinforces the message that friendship can cross class divides, as the twins admire each other for differences that are linked to their social class in this song.
- 'Miss Jones' reflects the way that working-class people were more seriously affected by the economic crises of the late 20th century than middle-class employers like Mr Lyons.

Page 36: Language in 'Blood Brothers'

1.   E.g. Their use of language, such as the omission of 'g' from "movin'", reflects the speech of working-class people in Liverpool at the time. / Russell uses non-standard spellings like "gorra" to reflect their regional accents.
2.   E.g. His use of omission when he says "An'" and "y'" makes his speech sound informal. This contrasts with his use of formal words and sentence structures elsewhere in the scene.
3.   Repetition: e.g. The repetition of the bad omen makes it seem as though bad luck is unavoidable.
     Rhyme: e.g. The rhyme pattern makes Sammy's speech sound more haunting and gives it a sinister tone.
     Metaphor: e.g. Mrs Lyons' idea about taking a twin is described as a seed that can "Take root and grow".
     E.g. This reflects the way the idea takes on a life of its own.
4.   E.g. Russell uses ellipses to make her sentences disjointed. This makes her thoughts seem scattered and suggests that she is frantic. / Mrs Lyons' speech is full of short, abrupt commands and accusations, which makes her seem agitated.

Page 37: Atmosphere and Mood

1.   E.g. He uses a repeated "*bass note*" to create a "*heartbeat*" that gets more and more intense. The heartbeat is unsettling because it suggests that the pact will become a matter of life and death.
2.   optimistic: e.g. when Mrs Johnstone claims that life will be better in Skelmersdale
     humorous: e.g. when the twins talk about Sammy having a plate in his head
     sad: e.g. when Linda feels helpless during Mickey's arrest
3.   E.g. His repetition of "There's gypsies in the wood" highlights Mrs Lyons' paranoia that Edward is going to be stolen from her, while his references to the devil suggest that she is being pursued by something evil.
4.   E.g. The repetition of "There's a mad man" emphasises Mickey's loss of control. This phrase is full of short words, so the repetition of it increases the pace of the scene, making Mickey's search seem more frantic.
Task: Here are some points you could have included:
- The mood changes from playful to tense during the scene where Mrs Lyons finds out about Edward's locket. Russell introduces background music to hint that something dramatic is going to happen, which makes the audience feel tense. Mrs Lyons' series of questions adds to the tension by making it seem like she's interrogating Edward.
- The mood changes from frantic to solemn when Mickey is caught after the petrol station robbery. Mickey's repetition of "You shot him" creates a frantic mood, which becomes solemn when he is shown "*silently crying*" after he has been caught. The fact that Mickey "*remains*" even though Sammy runs away physically slows down the pace of the scene,

Answers

contributing to the solemn mood.

Page 38: Imagery and Symbolism

1. a) Dancing / Marilyn Monroe.
   b) Any valid explanation, e.g. Dancing no longer symbolises happiness as it comes to represent Mickey's mental instability. / Marilyn Monroe becomes a symbol for Mickey's addiction and depression.
      E.g. Dancing — "His mind's gone dancing"
      Marilyn Monroe — "treats his ills with daily pills / Just like Marilyn Monroe"
2. E.g. The images of superstition, such as a "lone magpie" and a cracked mirror, are related to bad luck, creating an ominous atmosphere.
3. E.g. Russell makes it seem like an important ceremony as the boys make an oath and clasp hands.
4. E.g. The Narrator associates innocence and freedom with the spring and summer. He then links the effects of Linda's pregnancy to poor weather that spoils these warmer seasons, saying that "the sun began to fade" and "the rain came falling down".

Page 39: 'Blood Brothers' on the Stage

1. a) E.g. It makes their pretend violence seem less innocent, as the audience has already seen that the play ends with real violence.
   b) E.g. Mickey and Linda's struggle seems sadder, as the audience has seen the same actors playing carefree children.
2. a) E.g. "*Music is quietly introduced.*"
      Any valid explanation, e.g. It creates an emotional atmosphere that makes their parting seem sadder.
   b) E.g. "*On a punctuated note* Mrs Lyons *lunges again*"
      Any valid explanation, e.g. Mrs Lyons' lunge is matched by the abrupt note, making her action seem more sudden and more powerful.
3. E.g. It encourages the audience to compare the similarities and differences between the two families' lives.
4. E.g. To avoid the need for scene changes that would stop the play's action from flowing smoothly. / To create a neutral space where characters from different classes can interact.

Page 40: Skills Focus — Staging and Dramatic Techniques

1. a) E.g. He is "*on a platform*" which suggests that he is important. / The fact that he has an "*audience*" suggests that lots of people are interested in what he has to say.
   b) E.g. Both Mickey and Edward pause before "*eventually*" speaking. These hesitations suggest that they are unsure of what to say.
2. E.g. They both involve a lot of movement, emphasising Mrs Lyons' desperation to get rid of Mickey. The fact that he is "*pursued*" makes Mrs Lyons seem almost predatory.
3. E.g. "*awed*", "*clueless*", "*greatly impressed*"
   The stage directions show that Edward is easily impressed and excited by new things. This suggests that he had a sheltered life before he met the Johnstones.

Page 41: Practice Questions

Your answers should have an introduction, several paragraphs developing different ideas and a conclusion.
You may have covered some of the following points:

1. • Russell presents the set as static in order to make characters seem powerless. He structures the events of Act One so that seven-year-old Mickey is shown knocking at the Johnstones' door just after Mrs Johnstone has gone through it after being fired. The fact that the set that surrounds Mrs Johnstone is unchanged makes it seem as though seven years have passed instantly, showing that she cannot stop time advancing. Her powerlessness reinforces the idea that she is hurtling towards the play's unavoidable tragic ending.

• Russell presents the reality of Skelmersdale as different from Mrs Johnstone's idealised view of it. In Act One, she hopes that the move will allow her to "wash" away "the muck an' the dirt an' the bloody trouble" of her estate. This unbroken list of contaminants emphasises her hope that Skelmersdale will provide a 'cleaner', more privileged, life. However, her song at the start of Act Two is interrupted by the neighbours' offstage argument, suggesting that the move has not provided her with the idyllic lifestyle she had dreamed of. Mrs Johnstone's inability to change her situation reflects the fact that many working-class people had few chances to improve their lives in the late 20th century.

• Russell presents the location of Edward's house as superior to that of Mickey's house, allowing him to explore ideas about class division. In Act One, Edward lives in a big house "up" in the park, while Mickey lives "down" from the park. This positioning emphasises the fact that Edward is 'above' Mickey in the social hierarchy. This separation is reinforced in Act Two: Edward's house is on a hill overlooking Mickey's estate, which suggests that the social gulf between them is even greater in Skelmersdale than in Liverpool.

2. • Russell uses music to create tension in the play. When Edward goes missing in Act One, Russell introduces music that ends with a "*percussion build to a sudden full stop*". This "*build*" creates tension because it suggests that something is about to happen, while the "*sudden*" stop creates a tense silence as the scene changes. This use of music adds to the tension created earlier in the scene through the Narrator's lyrics about the devil "creeping" closer to Mrs Lyons.

• The Narrator uses imagery of death, which builds tension. In Act Two, he describes Linda and the twins as "lambs in spring" who don't know the "fate the later seasons bring". Likening the children to "lambs" in this metaphor makes them seem like innocent animals bound for slaughter, highlighting their helplessness. This increases the tension by reminding the audience of the twins' unavoidable fate. The language Russell uses to describe death also creates tension in the play's first scene, in which the word "slain", which is usually applied to the murder of a beast, is used to suggest that a violent death awaits the twins.

• The fact that events covering a twenty-year period happen in the same space builds tension. After losing his job, Mickey argues with Edward about money in the same place on stage where he defended Edward when Sammy called him a "poshy". This highlights how Mickey has become more aware of the class divides that separated men like him and Edward in the late 20th century and creates tension by showing how much their relationship has deteriorated. The fact that the same actors play the twins throughout the play makes this deterioration more obvious, further increasing the tension for the audience.

3. • Russell uses songs to present class differences. In the song 'My Child', Mrs Johnstone fantasises about her child's clothes being "(supplied by) / George Henry Lee", an expensive department store, if he is middle class. By using the passive verb "supplied", Mrs Johnstone suggests that middle-class people receive goods as if by right. This emphasises her belief that people from the middle class live a life of ease compared to those of her own class. Later in the play, the twins use the melody from 'My Child' in the song 'My Friend' to celebrate their class differences, which suggests that, unlike Mrs Johnstone, they don't believe that middle-class life is superior.

• Russell uses the twins' adult lives to present the inequality caused by class differences. Russell structures the play so that Edward describes how "fantastic" university is immediately after Mickey is made redundant. This contrast between Edward's success in higher education and Mickey's unemployment highlights the fact that working-class people in the 1970s and 1980s had fewer opportunities to improve

Answers

their lives than people belonging to the middle class. This reinforces Russell's idea that a person's upbringing has a big impact on their identity.

- Sequential scenes are used to present class differences. In Act One, Russell structures the play so that Mrs Lyons is given "fifty pounds" shortly after Mrs Johnstone's children repeatedly demand to look in "the catalogue". These demands highlight the financial pressures Mrs Johnstone faces as a working-class single mother, while the repetition of "catalogue" shows that she must use credit (a loan) to buy things. The fact that Mrs Lyons obtains money quickly from her husband shortly afterwards emphasises how much easier her situation is. These scenes reflect the vast differences in wealth that existed between the classes in the late 20th century.

4.
- The conflict between Mrs Johnstone and Mrs Lyons is shown to be an effect of Mrs Lyons' paranoia. While Mrs Lyons searches for a knife in Act Two, she claims that Mrs Johnstone is "like a shadow" that won't go away. The word "shadow" in this comparison implies that Mrs Lyons sees Mrs Johnstone, who is also Edward's mother, as a dark and threatening version of herself. The threat she imagines that Mrs Johnstone poses is therefore shown to be a cause of violent conflict between them. This scene suggests that Mrs Lyons' paranoia has become more disruptive as it had previously only caused minor conflict within her family home.
- Russell uses language to present the power imbalance between Mrs Lyons and Mrs Johnstone. When Mrs Lyons sacks Mrs Johnstone in Act One, Mrs Johnstone responds by saying "All right. All right, Mrs Lyons, right." The commas and full stops break up Mrs Johnstone's dialogue into short chunks, making her speech sound hesitant, while her repetition of "right" shows she is unsure what to say, highlighting her powerlessness to challenge Mrs Lyons. This scene reflects the way that, in the late 20th century, the job security of the working class often depended on the needs of their middle-class employers.
- Russell uses stage directions to increase the tension between Mrs Lyons and Mrs Johnstone. In Act One when Mrs Johnstone tries to take Edward back, Mrs Lyons *roughly drags* her away from the cot. Through this aggressive action, their confrontation shifts from a verbal to a physical one, heightening the tension between them. This tension is further increased in Act Two when Mrs Lyons *lunges* at Mrs Johnstone with murderous intent, showing how serious their conflict has become.

5.
- Russell gives the play elements of a classical tragedy to create an atmosphere of doom. In Act Two, after the twins are reunited, the Narrator fulfils the role of a classical chorus when he comments on the action, warning that "the reckoning day" is coming. The phrase "reckoning day" refers to the religious belief that everyone will be judged for their actions on Judgement Day. The suggestion that Mrs Lyons and Mrs Johnstone will soon face the tragic consequences of their actions creates a menacing atmosphere. This heightens the sense of doom created by the opening scene, in which the Narrator reveals the play's tragic ending.
- Russell creates a humorous atmosphere to highlight childhood innocence. When Mickey and Linda go to get Edward, Mickey speaks *"loud but conspiratorially"* to Edward. This stage direction creates humour, as the word *"conspiratorially"* suggests that Mickey is trying to be secretive, which contrasts with his *"loud"* delivery of the line. Here, Mickey's lack of awareness makes him seem childish and innocent. Russell structures the play so that the humour created by Mickey's innocence in this scene relieves the tension of the previous scene, in which an innocent childhood game results in conflict.
- Russell creates an atmosphere of despair to show the extent of Mickey's depression. In Act Two, Mickey's admission that he takes pills so that he can be "invisible" is followed

by a *"Pause"*. The word "invisible" suggests that Mickey wants to fade away out of view, hinting that he has given up, while the pause creates silence on stage, which generates an atmosphere of quiet despair. This highlights the depth of Mickey's depression. Mickey's plight in this scene reflects the impact of the economic decline of the 1970s and 1980s, which led to rising depression among the working class.

Section Five — Exam Buster

Page 42: Understanding the Question

1. b) <u>Explain</u> the <u>significance</u> of <u>Edward</u> in *Blood Brothers*.
   c) <u>Explain</u> <u>how</u> the theme of <u>fate</u> is <u>explored</u> in *Blood Brothers*.
   d) <u>How</u> is <u>staging</u> used to create <u>tension</u> in *Blood Brothers*?
   e) <u>Explain</u> <u>how</u> the <u>importance</u> of <u>class division</u> is <u>explored</u> in the play.
   f) <u>How</u> is the character of <u>Mickey</u> <u>presented</u> in *Blood Brothers*?
   g) <u>Explain</u> <u>why</u> <u>Linda</u> <u>changes</u> in the play.
2. a - 5, b - 1, c - 4, d - 2, e - 3

Page 43: Making a Rough Plan

1. E.g. Childhood friendship breaks down class barriers. / Linda's loyalty to Mickey is used to explore the strength of friendship. / Russell uses Mickey's influence on Edward to explore the impact of friendship on identity.
2. Pick your three most important points and put them in a sensible order. Write down a quote or an example from the play that backs them up.

Page 44: Making Links

1. Mickey and Sammy are very different despite having the same upbringing. E.g. Mickey tries to stop Sammy from robbing the bus conductor.
   Mickey experiences prejudice because of his upbringing. E.g. Mrs Lyons judges Mickey on his background.
   Edward's good manners highlight his middle-class upbringing. E.g. Mrs Lyons is appalled when she hears Edward swear.
2. E.g. If one of your points was 'Childhood friendship breaks down class barriers' and your evidence was that Mickey and Edward are friends even though they have different social backgrounds, you could link it to the fact that they don't just accept each other's differences; they actively admire them.

Page 45: Structuring Your Answer

1. E.g. Point: Russell suggests that a person's upbringing can't erase their natural identity.
   Example: For example, Mrs Lyons wants to move away from Liverpool because she thinks that Edward is "drawn to" the Johnstones.
   Explain: This highlights her concern that his natural identity will prove stronger than the middle-class upbringing that she has tried to give him.
   Develop: Russell reinforces the idea that Edward's natural identity is still intact by highlighting similarities between the twins throughout the play.
2. a) Edward thinks that misbehaving would be "super fun".
   b) Mickey thinks that Edward is still "a kid".
3. E.g. Point: Childhood friendship breaks down class barriers.
   Example: Unlike Sammy, Mickey doesn't care that Edward is a "poshy".
   Explain: This shows Mickey's lack of prejudice compared with his older brother, who has already learned to discriminate based on class.
   Develop: As an adult, Mickey comes to resent Edward's privilege, reinforcing the idea that children are less aware of class barriers.

Answers

Page 46: Introductions and Conclusions

1. Intro b) is better, e.g. Intro a) makes points which aren't relevant to the question, such as the reference to superstition.
2. E.g. The first and last sentences should be made relevant to the question by mentioning how these points are linked to the theme of fate. No new points should be introduced — the conclusion should give a summary of the points already made in the essay.

Task: Your introduction and conclusion should both give a clear answer to the question. The introduction should include your main points, but no evidence. Your conclusion should summarise your argument and not include new points.

Page 47: Writing about Context

1. a - 2, b - 3, c - 1
2. Contextual information: families who were moved to New Towns like Skelmersdale in the 1960s had no control over where they were sent.
    You could have included context as the Explain or Develop part of the paragraph. The context you wrote about should be relevant to your Point and linked to the Example.

Page 48: Linking Ideas and Paragraphs

1. E.g. In the play, Edward often forgets how privileged he is. For example, in Act Two, Edward asks Mickey "why is a job so important?" This suggests that Edward struggles to understand what life is like for Mickey, as he has never experienced poverty. Later in the scene, Edward and Mickey's relationship breaks down when he tries to give Mickey money.
2. You should have used the P.E.E.D. structure and included connecting words and phrases such as 'therefore' or 'for example' to link your ideas.
3. E.g. Russell also explores the theme of friendship by...
    This idea is developed further when...

Page 49: Marking Answer Extracts

1. 4-5: The answer integrates an appropriate example from the text and shows an understanding of contextual factors. However, the analysis of Russell's language isn't detailed enough for it to be a 6-7 answer. There are some grammar, spelling and punctuation errors, and the range of vocabulary and sentence structures is limited.

Page 50: Marking Answer Extracts

1. a) 8-9: E.g. "In Act One, she hits Edward... emphasises her unpleasant nature to the audience." — closely and perceptively analyses how the writer uses language to create meaning "Later in the play... makes Mrs Lyons' behaviour seem even more manipulative to the audience." — detailed exploration of the relationship between the text and its context
   b) 6-7: E.g. "However, she quickly becomes... taking away her children." — integrated, well-chosen examples "When Mrs Johnstone is upset... heavy persuasion." — thorough exploration of how the writer uses structure

Pages 51-52: Marking a Whole Answer

1. 8-9: E.g. The answer examines several different aspects of context in detail, including gender roles and class. There is close and perceptive analysis of language, for example the examination of the word "domain" in the third paragraph.

Page 53: Skills Focus — Writing Well

1. The Narrator changes his atitude [attitude] towards Mrs Johnstone by the end of the play. At the start of Act one [One], he suggests that she is a "cruel" and stone-hearted mother, but in the final seen [scene], he suggested [suggests] that "class" might actually be to blame for the twins [twins'] deaths. This implys [implies] that Mrs Johnstone is not fully

responsable [responsible] and shows that the Narrator's opinion has changed.

2. You could have rewritten the sentences as follows:
    a) Edward is a source of conflict between Mrs Johnstone and Mrs Lyons.
    b) Mrs Lyons irritates Mr Lyons several times during the play.
    c) Mickey, Edward and Linda's childhood friendship is strong.
    d) Russell uses structure effectively to create tension in the play.

Page 54: Practice Questions

Your answers should have an introduction, several paragraphs developing different ideas and a conclusion.
You may have covered some of the following points:

1. • Russell uses Mr Lyons' attitude to money to highlight the wealth of the middle class. In the scene where Mrs Lyons asks for "fifty pounds", Mr Lyons asks "My God, what for?", then promptly gives her the money. Mr Lyons' surprise suggests that he considers "fifty pounds" a lot of money, however the fact that he hands it over straight away shows that he has immediate access to it and can afford to spend it. In Act Two, Mickey helps with a robbery to gain "Fifty notes", showing that he must resort to crime to access the same sort of money that middle-class people take for granted.
    • Mrs Lyons sees money as a source of power. When trying to bribe Mrs Johnstone in Act Two, she tells her she can offer her "Thousands..." The ellipsis after "Thousands" suggests that she wants the generosity of her offer to sink in, implying that she thinks it will have a powerful effect on Mrs Johnstone. This belief that money can grant power reflects the fact that the middle class in the late 20th century often used their wealth to gain a social advantage, for instance by educating their children privately.
    • Russell uses staging to highlight Mickey's unwillingness to accept charity. In Act Two, when Edward tries to give him money, Mickey quickly *throws the notes* away and tells Edward to "stuff it". Mickey therefore verbally and physically rejects the money at the same time, which makes his objection to Edward's charity seem more forceful. This contrasts with his willingness to accept sweets from Edward in Act One, which suggests that as he becomes more aware of Edward's privilege, he becomes less willing to accept his charity.

2. • Russell uses staging to demonstrate the innocence of childhood. When Mickey and Linda play in the street, the children get up after an explosion "*tops them all*". Russell's use of the slang word "*tops*" to describe killing makes the children's 'deaths' seem casual, while the fact that they are 'killed' several times on stage shows that they are innocent about the permanent nature of death. In Act Two, Mickey and Sammy face serious and permanent consequences after the robbery, which shows that their innocence has disappeared.
    • Linda, Mickey and Edward's relationship highlights the simplicity of childhood friendship. Just after meeting Edward, Linda refers to herself and the twins as a "gang", while the twins become blood brothers within minutes of knowing each other. By structuring these scenes in this way, Russell shows how quickly the children make friends. In contrast, when the characters become teenagers, their friendship is complicated by the twins' feelings for Linda. This makes their childhood friendship seem even more simple in comparison.
    • Russell uses Linda and the twins to suggest that gender can be insignificant for children. In Act One, seven-year-old Mickey tells Edward that Linda is "a girl but she's all right". Mickey's use of the word "but" suggests that he knows that being a girl and being "all right" are meant to be contradictions, but he doesn't mind. Russell uses Mickey's attitude to suggest that children are not restricted by the gender roles that often dictated the behaviour of adults in the late 20th century.

Answers

3.
- The Narrator is used to change the mood of the montage that shows Linda and the twins' teenage years. In this montage, Linda and the twins enjoy a series of leisure activities. This quick succession of scenes makes them seem carefree by implying that fun is the most important thing in their lives. This reflects the idea that originated in the 1960s that teenagers are a distinct group with a unique sense of freedom and hope. However, the Narrator's ominous commentary at the same time introduces a menacing tone. This heightens the play's tragic mood as the twins' fate seems more cruel to the audience once they have seen them as carefree teenagers.
- Russell uses Mrs Lyons' distress to introduce a mood of panic. In Act One, when Edward goes missing, she calls "Edward, Edward, Edward..." as soon as she is on stage. This repetition of a single word, which is separated only by commas, increases the pace of Mrs Lyons' dialogue and suggests that she is too frantic to wait for a response, giving the impression that she is trapped in a cycle of panic. This contrasts with the light-hearted mood of the previous scene. Russell's use of structure heightens this distress as Mrs Lyons begins to shout as soon as Edward leaves the stage, making her panic seem more immediate.
- Russell uses a mood change to suggest that Mrs Johnstone's happiness won't last. In Act Two, Russell structures the play so that scenes of her happy life in Skelmersdale are immediately followed by the Conductor's rhetorical questions "Happy are y'? Content at last?" These questions suggest that her happiness is not guaranteed, which creates a sense of unease that taints the previously light-hearted mood. The part of the Conductor is played by the Narrator, which makes this mood change more effective as he is associated with the twins' doom in the play's first scene.

4.
- Mickey and Sammy are used to represent other working-class children at the time the play is set. This is particularly apparent during the game in Act One; some of the children, are unnamed and others are only referred to as "Kid". This sets up the expectation with the audience that these children, and all other working-class children, will face similar difficulties to those faced by Mickey and Sammy. The idea that an entire group is limited by their social class highlights how widespread the problems faced by the working-class were in the late 20th century.
- Russell uses Mickey to show that working-class children had few opportunities in the late 20th century. Mickey's school is *all boredom and futility*. By using *futility*, a formal, 'adult' word to describe the pointless atmosphere of Mickey's school, Russell suggests that society as a whole, not just the class in Mickey's school, considers education to be a waste of time for working-class children. This reflects the fact that working-class children were expected to get low-paid jobs as soon as they left school, rather than using school as a stepping stone to university. Earlier in the act, Russell uses staging to hint at Mickey's lack of opportunities as he goes to school on the same bus that Sammy takes to the unemployment office.
- Russell uses structure to show that the working class, represented by Mickey, faced police prejudice in the late 20th century. In Act One, the Policeman threatens Mrs Johnstone and says that Mickey nearly committed "a serious crime", but, in the next scene, he shows respect to Mr Lyons and dismisses Edward's behaviour as a "prank". These sequential scenes highlight the Policeman's prejudice by emphasising the way that he treats Mickey more harshly than Edward. The Policeman also judges Mickey based on Sammy's bad reputation in this scene, showing that Mickey faces prejudice because of his specific family background as well as his social class.

5.
- Russell uses the character of Linda to add humour to the play. In Act Two, she proudly announces that she has been to see "*Nymphomaniac Nights*" and "*Swedish Au Pairs*" immediately after Mickey and Edward try to hide the fact that they've seen them. This creates humour because Linda's openness contrasts with Mickey and Edward's reluctance to admit that they've seen the films. Russell may have used Linda to add this humour to relieve the tension created in the previous scene in which Mrs Lyons attacks Mrs Johnstone.
- Russell uses Linda to highlight the lack of freedom that many women experienced at the time when *Blood Brothers* is set. In Act Two, the Narrator says Linda wants to be set free from washing "a million dishes". This hyperbolic language exaggerates Linda's workload, suggesting that she will never be free of her duties. This reflects the burden of the domestic chores that many working-class women carried in the late 20th century. Earlier in the play, Linda is portrayed as a carefree child and teenager, which makes her loss of freedom towards the end of the play seem more significant.
- Linda's affair with Edward moves the plot towards its tragic conclusion. Russell structures the play so that Mickey learns of Linda and Edward's betrayal and searches for Edward immediately after the affair is revealed to the audience. This all happens in a short space of time, which increases the pace of the play and makes it seem as though the characters are being propelled towards the tragic ending. This is consistent with the classical tragic form that Russell adapts in the play; the destinies of the characters in classical tragedies are very often governed by forces outside their control.

The Characters from 'Blood Brothers'

Phew! After tackling all those questions, I reckon you deserve a bit of a break. So grab a cup of tea and your favourite kind of biscuit, make yourself comfortable and enjoy *Blood Brothers* — *The Cartoon...*

Mrs Johnstone

Mickey Johnstone

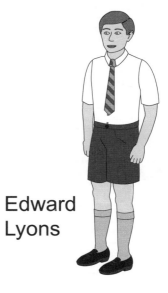

Edward Lyons

Mrs Lyons

Mr Lyons

Sammy Johnstone

Linda

Narrator

Willy Russell's 'Blood Brothers'